The Pattern of
VERTEBRATE EVOLUTION

UNIVERSITY REVIEWS IN BIOLOGY

General Editor: J. E. TREHERNE
Advisory Editors: Sir VINCENT WIGGLESWORTH F.R.S.
M. J. WELLS   T. WEIS-FOGH

ALREADY PUBLISHED

1. The Behaviour of Arthropods — J. D. Carthy
2. The Biology of Hemichordata and Protochordata — E. J. W. Barrington
3. The Physiology of Nematodes — D. L. Lee
4. The Metabolism of Insects — Darcy Gilmour
5. Reproduction in the Insects — K. J. Davey
6. Cybernetics and Biology — F. H. George
7. The Physiology of Trematodes — J. D. Smyth
8. Aspects of the Physiology of Crustacea — A. P. M. Lockwood
9. The Physiology of Sense Organs — DeForest Mellon Jr
10. The Pattern of Vertebrate Evolution — L. B. Halstead

IN PREPARATION

The Physiology of Cestodes — J. D. Smyth
Venoms and Venomous Animals — F. E. Russell
The Biology of Brachiopods — M. Rudwick
Physical Concepts in Biology — J. W. L. Beament
Cell Biology — A. V. Grimstone
The Biology of Echinoderms — E. J. Binyon
The Physiology of Nerve and Muscle — T. I. Shaw
The Permeability of Living Membranes — J. Dainty

The Pattern of
VERTEBRATE
EVOLUTION

L. B. HALSTEAD
University of Reading

W. H. FREEMAN AND COMPANY
SAN FRANCISCO

To Beryl

OLIVER AND BOYD LTD
Tweeddale Court Edinburgh W.1

First Published 1968
© 1968 L. B. Halstead

Library of Congress
 Catalog Card No. 69–18524

Printed in Great Britain by
Bell and Bain Limited Glasgow

Preface

You can't solve a problem? Well, get down and investigate the present facts and its past history!   Mao Tse-Tung

The recorded history of the vertebrates spans a period of 500 million years. The purpose of this book is not to catalogue the development and subsequent progress of all the major groups but to explore a number of events and associated phenomena in depth. Even so the choice of the subjects covered is essentially personal, reflecting my own particular interests, which range from the origin of the vertebrates to the future of man. As we have no direct knowledge of either, the first and last chapters are necessarily more speculative than the intervening fifteen. Nevertheless in both cases there is enough indirect evidence to justify some conclusions. Time will serve to demonstrate the validity of my predictions on the future of man!

The way in which the vertebrates might have first evolved is outlined, with descriptions of the earliest known vertebrate fossils, and then the reasons for the development of bone, the characteristic and important tissue, are discussed. The success of the vertebrates is linked with their endoskeleton and with their teeth. This has led me to consider the original functions and early evolution of bone and dentine. As the latter formed the skin of the early vertebrates and was later restricted to the teeth, its history has some relevance to the dental sciences as does that of bone to the study of the living tissue. It was at this early stage of evolution that the basic vertebrate pattern became established; and this fact prompts a somewhat detailed discussion of the internal anatomy of the earliest forms.

The subsequent history of the vertebrates is clearly displayed in the fossil record, and this book is concerned with the reasons behind the changes that took place as the various major types evolved. Key points are examined in the context of the conditions in which they took place and not, in traditional fashion, regarded as part of some inexorable and purposive progress. Many of the great events and the slow changes associated with them have been regarded as pre-adaptive. Nevertheless, in all cases it is possible to demonstrate, with reasonable confidence, that the changes actually conferred some advantage on the animals concerned immediately and within their original environments; there is never the faintest hint of anticipatory evolution. A number of basic principles seem to underlie the pattern of the fossil record. Evolution takes place on a broad front with little concern for "natural" phyletic classification. Almost all (the birds are a possible exception) the vertebrate classes are polyphyletic in origin. The morphological boundaries are crossed by more than one lineage. In addition, another and rarely mentioned facet of the mechanisms of evolution, the development of food chains, is discussed.

The perennial problem of the extinction of the dinosaurs, for which no sensible solution has yet been advanced, receives only light-hearted treatment.

Man's origin and evolution form the subject of the concluding chapters. Recent work on primate behaviour suggests a revised definition of *Homo sapiens*: man, the weapon-maker, since his unique contribution to evolution is the technique and habit of making weapons for future use. Finally I suggest that a number of basic human traits can be attributed to our group hunting predator ancestry; and their consequences, as shown by trends in contemporary society, are then extrapolated into the future.

This book is concerned more with the interpretation of data than with its documentation. Its purpose will have been achieved if it proves thought-provoking and convinces the reader that palaeontology is an integral part of the study of living things.

Chart A is a simplified geological time scale with the ranges of the major vertebrate classes; Chart B shows a family tree of the chordates based on the approach and interpretations in this book.

CAINOZOIC
   QUATERNARY
      Pleistocene   1·5 — 2

   TERTIARY
      Pliocene   7
      Miocene   26
      Oligocene   37 — 38
      Eocene   53 — 54
      Palaeocene   65

MESOZOIC
   CRETACEOUS   136
   JURASSIC   190 — 195
   TRIASSIC   225

PALAEOZOIC
   PERMIAN   280
   CARBONIFEROUS   345
   DEVONIAN   395
   SILURIAN   430 — 440
   ORDOVICIAN   500
   CAMBRIAN   570

"PROTOCHORDATA" AGNATHA PISCES AMPHIBIA REPTILIA AVES MAMMALIA

CHART A

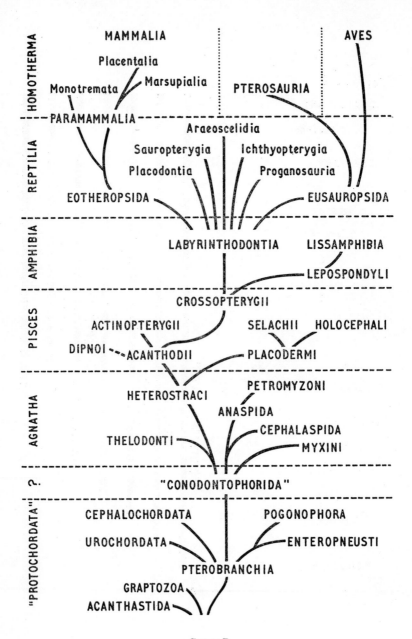

Chart B

Acknowledgements

I am deeply indebted to my friend and colleague Dr. Karen Hiiemäe for her patient help in the arduous task of editing the first draft of this book. Comments and criticisms have been gratefully received from Professor P. Allen, Mrs. Iris Andreski, Professor H. J. J. Blackwood, Dr. C. B. Cox, Miss Brita Erholtz, Professor A. Graham, Dr. K. A. Kermack, Professor R. B. Lucas, Miss Jacqueline Morris, Mrs. Beryl Tarlo, Dr. K. S. Thomson and Miss Susan Turner, all of whom are absolved from any responsibility for the views I express.

The illustrations (except Figs. 7d–l, 33, 35c, 46) were prepared by Miss Jennifer Middleton, Medical Artist, Royal Dental Hospital. Mrs. Cherrie Bramwell helped in the preparation of the Index. Professor J. Maynard Smith (University of Sussex) kindly gave permission for his poem '*Struthiomimus*' to be published for the first time. Thanks are due to the authors who have allowed themselves to be quoted and their illustrations to be used.

Contents

PREFACE   v

ACKNOWLEDGEMENTS   ix

1. ORIGIN OF THE VERTEBRATES   1

    Non-vertebrate chordates; larval evolution; the fossil evidence; conodonts— ?planktonic protovertebrates; early environment of vertebrates; origin of bone

2. EARLIEST VERTEBRATES   18

    Heterostracans; cephalaspids; anaspids

3. SKIN, DENTINE AND TEETH   27

    Development of patterns of dermal armour; dentine—a primitive skin; origin of tooth cusps; teeth

4. BONE, CARTILAGE AND THE SKELETON   40

    Aspidin—the precursor of bone; cartilage *versus* bone; bone —a structural material; biomechanics of joints; the static and dynamic skeleton

5. BRAINS   57

    Agnathan brains; gnathostome brains

6. PRIMITIVE JAWED VERTEBRATES   65

    Head segmentation; acanthodian fish and jaws; arthrodires (placoderms) and cartilaginous fish; evolution of paired fins

7. FIRST LAND VERTEBRATES   77

    Transition from water to land; 'Choanichthyes'; first amphibian; the Age of amphibians; 'Eoreptilia'

8. EARLY REPTILES   92

    Origin of the amniote egg; classification of reptiles; temporal openings; a new classification

9. MAMMAL-LIKE REPTILES   103
   Distribution of paramammals; achievement of mammalian
   status; reptile/mammal boundary; evolution of terrestrial
   food chains

10. LIZARD *INTER-REGNUM*   115

11. AGE OF DINOSAURS   119
    Bipedal *versus* quadrupedal ancestry; dinosaurs

12. RETURN TO THE SEA   128
    Ichthyosaurs; placodonts; nothosaurs; plesiosaurs; mosa-
    saurs; evolution of marine food chains

13. CONQUEST OF THE AIR   139
    Pterosaurs; birds

14. EXTINCTION   146

15. MODERN MAMMALS   150
    Adaptive radiation; diet and dentition; terrestrial carnivores;
    aquatic carnivores; carnivore jaws; herbivores—browsers
    and grazers; elephants; herbivores—gnawers and nibblers;
    herbivore jaws; omnivores; history of carnivores; cats;
    dogs

16. MAN—THE WEAPON MAKER   167
    Arboreal adaptations; early primates; *Ramapithecus*—the
    first hominid; *Australopithecus* and '*Homo habilis*'; *Homo
    erectus*—the first religious man; *Homo sapiens* including
    Neanderthal Man; a definition of Man

17. THE FUTURE OF MAN   185

    REFERENCES   191

    INDEX   203

1 : Origin of the Vertebrates

Vertebrates are constructed on a simple basic plan, whose origin has exercised the minds of many zoologists and palaeontologists. Most invertebrate phyla have, at one time or another, been proposed as vertebrate ancestors, but none have proved to fill the role. A solution to this dilemma has recently been provided by Nursall[134] and owes much to a basic rethinking of the classic view of the mechanics of evolution. Traditionally, phyla and the classes within them are seen in terms of a phylogenetic tree. The phyla either branch off from a 'good solid trunk of common origin' or from another phylum of supposedly ancestral nature. Within limits, this approach is perfectly acceptable as a means of demonstrating vertebrate evolution where the major taxa evolved from one another and where the intermediate or bridging forms either existed or still survive. The obvious examples of intermediate types are the amphibians which link the fish and the reptiles, and the reptiles, which link the amphibians with the birds and the mammals. There is, however, no reason to suppose that the invertebrate phyla should show an equally clear series of steps connecting the protozoa with the earliest vertebrates. Indeed all the attempts to arrange the known invertebrates on a phylogenetic tree have, in the process, turned the tree into a complex and convoluted espalier. An exception to this is Nursall's thesis that there is no need to postulate a 'tree' at all, but rather a series of parallel evolutionary developments, all from a simple unicellular protist stage, which finally produce the various invertebrate phyla. This thesis presupposes the independence of the various phyla, but does not deny any degrees of affinity between them and allows for the possibility that the tree pattern of evolution did in fact pertain after the early stages.

Non-Vertebrate Chordates

Even if Nursall's view is in fact a correct explanation of vertebrate origins, it still leaves unanswered the problem of the relationship between them and the other members of the chordate phylum (Fig. 1). For full membership of the phylum Chordata, an animal is expected to possess, at least at some time during its life history, the following features: a notochord (a stiff rod of vacuolated cells), a dorsally situated tubular nerve cord, a perforated pharynx and a post-anal tail. On this count the cephalochordates (amphioxus), tunicates (or sea-squirts) and the vertebrates are all fully fledged members. Recently the chordates have been restricted to these three sub-phyla, and the hemichordates and pogonophores placed in two independent phyla separate from the chordates.[21] The hemichordates possess a perforated pharynx, which in the enteropneusts is clearly homologous both in structure and in function to that of the tunicates, cephalochordates and vertebrates. There is a concentration of nervous tissue in the mid-dorsal region of the collar which could perhaps be considered as the precursor of the tubular nerve cord. On the other hand, the stomochord can in no way be homologised with the notochord although in the past authors have attempted this. It is evident that the hemichordates belong to the chordate hierarchy, albeit at a low level. To place them in a separate phylum tends to obscure a real relationship, and leads one subconsciously to emphasise the differences rather than the similarities, which in this instance are the more significant. Exactly the same problem arises with the pogonophores (which are, admittedly, incredibly aberrant) as they have no gut and digestion takes place outside the body. Ivanov,[88] who has made the major contribution on these animals, has claimed for them the status of an independent phylum. But once again, as with the hemichordates, such a procedure automatically stresses the differences between the various groups, whereas it is the similarities that need to be emphasised. For all their aberrant nature, the pogonophores do show a number of similarities to the hemichordates, and it follows, if the criteria for including the hemichordates in the phylum Chordata are accepted, that the pogonophores also must be included in the latter group. In the present work, the subphyla Hemichordata, Pogonophora, Urochordata (Tunicata), Cephalochordata, and Craniata (Vertebrata) are included in the phylum Chordata.

Before considering the possible relationship of the vertebrates to the above groups, it is necessary to decide exactly what features are connected with the achievement of vertebrate status. The notochord, which in the gnathostomes (jawed vertebrates) forms the template for the future vertebral column, is present in the tail of larval tunicates and in amphioxus, where it forms an internal supporting skeleton. This gives the body some degree of rigidity on which the muscles can act. Motility in the larval tunicates and amphioxus is achieved by movement of the post-anal tail. In addition to the notochord and post-anal tail,

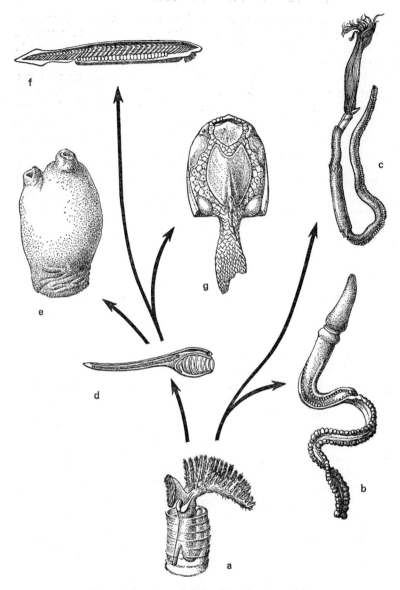

FIG. 1. Representative chordates (not to scale)
a. Pterobranch hemichordate; b. Enteropneust hemichordate; c. Pogonophore; d. 'Tadpole' larva; e. Tunicate; f. Cephalochordate;
g. Vertebrate.

these animals have a somatic musculature. These three characters are responsible for the active free-swimming life of the larval tunicate and of amphioxus. Animals with these characteristics should therefore be reasonable candidates for vertebrate ancestors.

The dorsal nerve cord is found in larval tunicates and in amphioxus, but it is not really possible to suggest any reason for this—only that it happens to be the hallmark of the vertebrates. These animals do not have highly developed sense organs. The larval tunicate has, for example, a statocyst (a simple organ of balance) and an eye spot. The larvae are at first positively phototropic and negatively geotropic (i.e. they swim up towards the light), thereafter the reverse holds, and they swim down to find a dark area on which to settle, usually the underside of a rocky ledge. The initial development of balancing and visual organs which characterise the vertebrates, may have resulted from the need to ensure adequate dispersal of the young. Sight and balance are, however, the two essential senses for an active life.

Equally, any animal feeding on microscopic particles suspended in water must have some means of distinguishing the edible from the merely inedible as well as the positively noxious; in other words a sense of smell. The organ of 'smell' in the adult tunicates is the neural gland and in amphioxus it is Hatschek's pit. By contrast with the other senses, the derivation of the olfactory seems to have been from a water-testing system, in all probability similar to that seen in animals living an essentially passive life.

The perforated pharynx is found in its simplest form in the pterobranch hemichordate *Cephalodiscus* (but not in *Rhabdopleura*). In the enteropneust hemichordates, tunicates and cephalochordates, the gill-bars and slits are built on exactly the same plan and their functions are identical; they are the main respiratory and feeding organs. The last two groups feed on microscopic particles which are swept into the pharynx by the action of cilia on the gill bars. Mucus, produced from the endostyle in the floor of the pharynx, traps the food particles and the water is passed out through the gill-slits. The mucus is then carried up the gill-bars until it reaches the epipharyngeal groove, whence it passes back to the oesophagus as a coiled and loaded rope. This type of passive microphagous feeding characterises all the lower chordates, including the larval lamprey or ammocoete. The perforated pharynx is a structure fundamentally associated with a sedentary mode of life, and more especially with ciliary feeding. Later, when muscle action replaces that of cilia and when the food taken becomes larger and hence more varied, the role of the perforated pharynx becomes essentially respiratory.

Any postulated vertebrate ancestor must, therefore, show two sets of basic features: one characteristic of a passive sessile ancestor, the other

	notochord	vertebral column	cranium bone	post-anal tail	segmental musculature	dorsal nerve cord	sense organs	perforated pharynx
Pterobranch hemichordates								
Enteropneust hemichordates								
Pogonophores								
Tunicates								
Larval tunicates								
Cephalochordates								
Agnathan vertebrates								
Gnathostome vertebrates								

TABLE I

acquired from an active free-swimming form.[177,182] However, to qualify fully for vertebrate status, an animal must in addition show well developed olfactory, optic and auditory sense organs, and some sort of bony or cartilaginous protection of the brain. The last, the cranium, gives the vertebrates their name Craniata, frequently preferred to Vertebrata since all vertebrates do not necessarily possess vertebrae. Indeed, vertebrae are not found until the development of the gnathostomes or jawed vertebrates, although no-one would deny the cyclostomes and ostracoderms full membership of the Vertebrata. Table I shows the presence of the features discussed among the different groups of chordates. It is evident that the major groups listed show a gradual increase in the number of vertebrate or protovertebrate features. Listing them in such a hierarchy seems justified, so long as this is not then interpreted as meaning that they are necessarily derived from one another in this particular order. It is possible to look at these different groups as a series of structural stages, showing a progressive increase in morphological complexity, which lead eventually to the vertebrates. However, when the larvae of some of these animals are studied, it is evident that in this particular scheme of organisation they rank incomparably higher than their own parents.

Larval Evolution

This state of affairs allows of two fundamentally opposed interpretations. If one rigidly adheres to Haekel's 'Biogenic Law' (i.e. that ontogeny recapitulates phylogeny), one is forced to conclude that the adult tunicates, for example, represent a 'degeneration', in that they must have abandoned a life of freedom for one of sessile passivity. However, this particular line of approach does not get us much farther forward with regard to the origin of the vertebrates; it simply suggests that the non-vertebrate chordates are secondarily derived from degenerate vertebrates. The problem of where the vertebrates came from in the first instance remains. In fact, there is an alternative way of looking at this question, which avoids pushing the origin of the vertebrates back into the unknown and which, if only for its economy of hypotheses, has much to recommend it. Stated in the simplest terms, it is suggested that the role of the larvae of marine animals, especially sessile ones, is essentially different from that of the adults. Furthermore, in view of this, natural selection and evolution are just as likely to affect the larvae as the adults. Larval evolution was in all likelihood the general rule. So much would seem plainly evident, but there was a great deal of difficulty in getting this basic idea accepted by zoologists brought up on the 'Biogenic Law'. The credit must go to Garstang[67,68] for his success in establishing the concept of larval evolution, which is now universally recognised as fundamental to our understanding of major advances in evolution. However, as Garstang himself recognised, larval evolution in itself is not enough, for sexual maturity must also be considered. Maturation of the gonads and subsequent reproduction while still otherwise morphologically in the larval stage (neoteny), is a fairly frequent phenomenon. Given a measure of larval evolution together with neoteny, a basically new group of animals can suddenly appear with the simultaneous extinction of a previously well established one.[75]

Perhaps the strongest evidence for this sequence of events having taken place in the past is to be found in the living tunicates. The simplest tunicates are the solitary or colonial ascidians, which are exclusively bottom-dwelling sessile forms but possess an active free-swimming, site-seeking, tadpole larva. The second group is the thaliaceans, which again includes both solitary and colonial forms. This latter group is, however, entirely planktonic, and on metamorphosis the adults remain in the plankton. The final group of tunicates is the larvaceans, or appendicularians, a group which was probably derived from the thaliaceans but in which metamorphosis is not completed. In this latter group, the basic larval form (muscular tail with the nerve cord overlying the notochord) is always retained in spite of the highly specialised nature of its feeding mechanism. In essence, these animals are neotenous tunicates, and, although extremely specialised, nevertheless indicate the possibility of a larval tunicate leading a life of its own and so, by inference, branching out into a protovertebrate. This state of affairs is not confined to the tunicates but is also to be found in the cephalo-chordates, where the amphioxides larva may spend up to three years in the plankton and grows to a considerable size, during which time its gonads almost ripen. Should the amphioxides larva become sexually mature, it would give rise to a race of 'near vertebrates'—although the anterior extension of the notochord which prevents the development of a proper brain would preclude it from real membership of the vertebrate club.[248]

If, as seems reasonable, one accepts that larval evolution coupled with neoteny has taken place at various times, then the possible origin of the vertebrates can be examined in this context, paying particular attention to those features which appear to herald the basic vertebrate features. The ascidian larva is simply a site-seeker and therefore needs an organ of propulsion—a muscular tail, with a stiffening rod or notochord, and also sense organs to give awareness of light and position (Fig. 2). The nervous system must be linked with the organ of loco-motion; hence the dorsal nerve cord. These are the essential elements of an active life and clearly foreshadow the vertebrate line. However, it is not really possible to consider the ascidian tadpole as a direct vertebrate ancestor as its site-seeking life is of short duration.[24] The larva does not feed—an essential prerequisite for any animal with evolutionary potentialities—and certainly there are no signs of any significant gonad development. It must be admitted that, despite this,

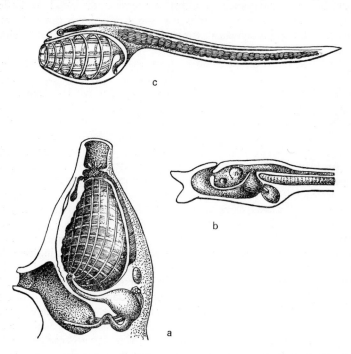

FIG. 2. a. Diagram of adult tunicate showing perforated pharynx; b. anterior part of 'tadpole' larva showing dorsal nerve cord and notochord; c. hypothetical pre-vertebrate 'tadpole' larva. (after Romer).

in the search for a vertebrate ancestor the ascidian tadpole is by far the most likely candidate and has almost all the right qualifications. The problem of reconciling the short active phase of larval life with the demands of a vertebrate ancestor is by no means insuperable; for there is no necessity to attempt to derive the vertebrates from the living ascidians. If such a derivation took place, it must have been a good many hundred million years ago. In view of this, it is surely reasonable to extrapolate the structure of an ascidian back to its simplest condition. When this is done, the result is a simple type of animal not far removed from a pterobranch hemichordate.[248] Indeed, it is a moot point whether such an animal would be a 'protoascidian' or a hemichordate. In fact, of course, it matters not one iota what term is used, so long as the type of animal under discussion is recognised. This having been said, a hemichordate ancestry for the vertebrates has a certain attraction, for the planktonic larvae spend a long time in the surface waters of the sea, so giving evolution a reasonable amount of time in which to accomplish things. The living hemichordates are not known to possess a tadpole larva, but this need not be the serious objection it at first appears. Presumably, those hemichordates that did have tadpoles gave rise to the higher chordates and, hence, eventually to the vertebrates. This is not as far-fetched as it may appear. A fully documented parallel is found in the lobe-finned fish, among which the lungfish and coelacanths survive, but not the more advanced and efficient rhipidistians, which died out in giving rise to the amphibians and hence all the higher vertebrates. This is not to say that the vertebrates necessarily originated from the hemichordates, but rather that they may have arisen from a hemichordate-like ancestor, or, as Dr. Mary Whitear[248] would prefer, from a 'protoascidian'.

The Fossil Evidence

A further approach to the problem of vertebrate origins is to examine the fossil record, in spite of numerous statements that such a search is by the very nature of things bound to be fruitless. Obviously a soft-bodied planktonic protovertebrate would stand precious little chance of being preserved; but sessile encrusting benthonic forms are quite a different matter. In fact, Kozlowski[106-9] has described in great detail the existence of a large and exceptionally varied fauna of pterobranch hemichordates including the graptolites, and even pogonophores, from rocks of the Ordovician period (some 500 million years ago) of Poland (Fig. 3). Their diversity is incomparably greater than the surviving *Rhabdopleura* and *Cephalodiscus* would suggest. There is indirect evidence that these sessile and encrusting pterobranchs had planktonic larvae—the sessile dendroid graptolites gave rise to the floating planktonic *Dictyonema* forms, and also to the 'true' graptolites, which were exclusively planktonic. From this the reasonable inference can be drawn that many of, if not all, the types of animal described by Kozlowski had planktonic larvae. It might be mentioned in parenthesis that both a rhabdopleurid and cephalodiscid are represented in the Polish sediments, and, as with their descendants, it is reasonable to assume also that they too possessed planktonic larvae. Unfortunately, it is quite impossible to suggest that the tadpole larva, and hence in every likelihood the vertebrates, arose from any particular group of pterobranch hemichordate described by Kozlowski, or even that the radiation he recorded represents the one out of which the vertebrates ultimately emerged. Nevertheless it seems likely that one could confidently expect the vertebrate stock to have emerged out of the sort

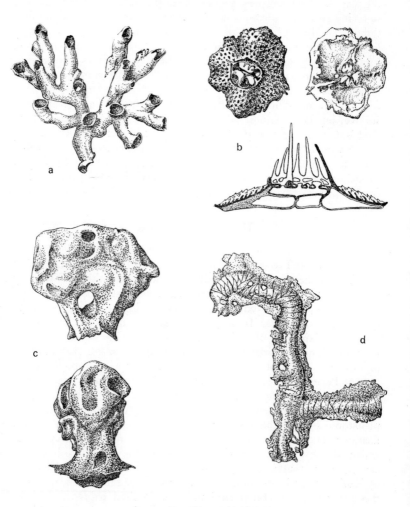

FIG. 3. Fossil hemichordates
a. Dendroid graptolite; b. Acanthastid; c. Cephalodiscid pterobranch;
d. Rhadbopleurid pterobranch. (after Kozlowski).

of radiation represented by the host of forms described by Kozlowski rather than from any 'famous' fossil.[213]

Major evolutionary advances are more likely to be found where there is evidence that radiations were occurring, clearly indicating periods of evolutionary activity. It may not be possible to pinpoint the ancestral form, but at least there will be the satisfaction of knowing its general whereabouts. In the story of vertebrate origins the fossil record lends its support, albeit in a minor key, to the theory of an ultimate hemichordate ancestry. Naturally, all this is entirely speculative, but it is at least a little gratifying that the evidence from both the living and the dead combines to give a reasonably coherent picture.

Conodonts? Planktonic Protovertebrates

It can be imagined that the first vertebrate or protovertebrate must have dwelt in the surface waters of the sea and been an active filter-feeder. This leads immediately to the question of whether there could possibly be any evidence of these first vertebrates in the fossil record. There is, in fact, a faint possibility that this stage in the history of the vertebrates may have been preserved in the form of the problematical microfossils, the conodonts. These fossils consist of calcium phosphate—a typically vertebrate hard tissue—deposited within soft tissue by the apposition of concentric layers, exactly as in primitive fish scales. There has been a great deal of controversy concerning the affinities of the 'Conodontophoridia'. It cannot even be said, without fear of contradiction, that they are of animal origin; for Fahlbusch[59] has claimed that they belong to algae! Conodonts have also been interpreted as phosphatic annelid jaws, fish teeth, gillrakers, gastropod radulae, nematode copulatory spicules and arthropod spines.[166] Since 1934 natural assemblages of conodonts have been described which appear to give some support to the view that they belonged to annelids, as they had a left and right symmetry.[166] It was believed that this must of necessity exclude them from the vertebrates, in particular the fish, which have upper and lower jaws. This objection does not, however, apply to the suggestion that these structures were the internal supports of a primitive branchial basket.

Recently Lindström[121] has interpreted the conodonts as part of a tentacular, or lophophore, feeding apparatus positioned beyond the animal's mouth. The direction of feeding currents in relation to the structures postulated by Lindström appears to be the exact reverse of that to be expected in any naturally occurring system. If, however, Lindström's directions are reversed and the whole apparatus enclosed within the body of the animal, the arrangement of feeding currents is identical to that found in the cephalochordates. If Lindström's restoration is correct, then it provides some slight evidence for the vertebrate, or at least protovertebrate, affinities of the conodont-bearing animal. For a long time it has been generally accepted that the conodonts belonged to planktonic animals, as they are associated with fossils from virtually every marine habitat; and it seems possible that they might have been a group of planktonic animals having hard parts of calcium phosphate and a feeding apparatus not unlike that of a protochordate or primitive vertebrate. The 'Conodontophoridia' can be tentatively interpreted as representing the first primitive filter-feeding, planktonic vertebrates.

Early Environment of the Vertebrates

From the evidence discussed it appears that the origin of the vertebrates was an event that took place in the sea. It has been argued, however, that genuine vertebrate status was achieved much later, and then only as a consequence of the initial colonisation of an entirely new environment—the fresh waters of rivers and lakes. It was the discovery of bony fragments in the Middle Ordovician Harding Sandstone of Colorado that provided the initial evidence for a freshwater habitat of the first vertebrates. Until these fossils were found, the prevailing view amongst zoologists was that the vertebrates had originated in the sea; this led to some difficulty, since geologists considered that the earliest vertebrate remains were of freshwater animals that had been swept downstream to burial at the river mouths. This interpretation was accepted by zoologists, who then advanced a number of theories to explain several basic vertebrate features on the basis that vertebrate life initially began in fresh waters.

There is a fundamental difference between the demands on an animal's body made by a freshwater, and those made by a saline environment. In the sea there is no appreciable osmotic gradient between the animal and its surroundings, the concentration of salts in the body fluids and in the sea water being essentially the same. In fresh water, however, the concentration of salts is almost negligible by comparison with that of body fluid and so an osmotic gradient is set up. This gradient will tend to produce water-logging of body tissues unless this intake is reduced to a minimum; consequently, if it is to survive in a freshwater habitat, an animal must have some water-proofing and a mechanism for the excretion of excess water. In the vertebrates this latter task is accomplished by the kidneys, and Homer Smith[194] has for many years championed the view that the origin of the glomerulus was a consequence of the initial colonisation of freshwaters by the early vertebrates and of the need to regulate the excess water entering the body by osmosis. He believed that one of the primary functions of the glomerular kidney was that of osmoregulation. In spite of considerable support for Homer Smith's ideas, it has been pointed out by Robertson[170] that organs based on the same principles as the glomerulus occur in a number of exclusively marine groups. Indeed, the hagfish (myxinoid cyclostomes) possess a glomerular kidney, and there is no evidence that they ever had a freshwater period in their history, for their blood is isotonic with seawater. The action of the glomerulus as a filter depends not on the osmotic gradient but simply on hydrostatic pressure. Naturally enough, it is not difficult to see how such a structure could readily take on the further function of osmoregulation. In fact, it is hard to imagine how the vertebrates could have conquered freshwaters without such an organ. This, however, is no reason for postulating the origin of the glomerular kidney as a direct response to the need for an osmoregulatory organ.

It appears that almost invariably in evolution a structure for survival under new conditions is already present or had begun its development in the original environment, although often for a different purpose. It can be a mistake to postulate that such a structure evolved in response to the functional demands eventually laid upon it.

The current situation is that zoologists have begun to discard the freshwater origin theories on purely zoological grounds. It may be asked what has become of the geological evidence in the meantime. This evidence too has seen some striking changes. The Harding Sandstone is now known to extend over many thousands of square miles and is interpreted as an offshore deposit.[55] This explains the water-worn nature of the bones which had been washed to and fro by the tides or by longshore drifting. In many ways it is rather unfortunate that so much attention should have been paid to the Harding Sandstone, since the first fossil vertebrates were found in Russia in the 1880s and were from Lower Ordovician rocks, being thus of earlier date than American forms. The Russian fossils came from glauconitic sands which are formed only in true marine conditions, although in shallow waters. The geological evidence has in fact always pointed unequivocally to an originally marine habitat for the first recorded vertebrates in the fossil record.[55]

The idea of a marine origin for the vertebrates is entirely consistent with what has already been surmised as the likely way in which the basic vertebrate animal first arose. The first unequivocal evidence of vertebrate fossils comes from near-shore sea deposits. Their existence is known only because these animals had evolved a bony carapace, from which it is fair to assume that they were no longer surface feeders in the plankton. They must, instead, have been detrital feeders on the sea-bed, and the most suitable region for such a mode of life is surely on the continental shelf, where the sea is shallow and light can penetrate. Life is likely to be at its most abundant and, especially near the beaches, ideal for scavengers. The change from an active planktonic life to an apparently somewhat restricted one as a mud-grubber was in all probability due to two interrelated factors—an increase in size coupled with the acquisition of a bony armour.

The Origin of Bone

The development of a bony tissue was of major significance in the evolution of the vertebrates. Without it, it would hardly have been possible to evolve into active predators, and certainly it would have been inconceivable to have taken up life on the land. In view of its subsequent importance in the later evolution of the vertebrates, it is perhaps worthwhile considering the possible reasons for its appearance at this very early stage of vertebrate history. Not surprisingly, there has been considerable speculation on this question. Most theories have been based on the assumption that the formation of an exoskeleton was a response to the taking up of life in freshwater. By far the most popular theory is that propounded by Romer,[173,179,181] who contends that, as its name 'armour' implies, it was for protection, in this instance against the dreaded pincers of the giant freshwater scorpions or eurypterids which inhabited the rivers and lakes of the time. According to Romer, these animals were the only serious rivals of the vertebrates. This theory suffers from one major drawback: although the later eurypterids and vertebrates certainly cohabited in lakes and rivers, the earliest vertebrates probably never saw a single eurypterid from one generation to the next. This is not to suggest that the function of the armour was not one of protection; there must certainly have been plenty of marine predators, to which a bony covering may have afforded some slight hindrance in their search for prey. However, it seems unlikely that the primary function was purely one of protection, since it was not simply a massive and impervious covering but was, instead, a rather spongy one, permeated by numerous anastomosing blood vessels and covered, at least initially, by a soft epidermal 'skin'. Homer Smith[194] saw in the bony armour evidence of a waterproofing mechanism. He imagined that it provided an impervious layer on the outside of the animals, although in fact it was spongy and had canals opening to the exterior. Naturally these external openings must have been covered by soft tissues during life and it may well be that the mucus exuded from the pores could have had some kind of waterproofing function, as it appears to have in the lamprey today. Whatever else its function, the bony carapace itself could hardly have served as a waterproofing agent. In any event it was present before the ostracoderms colonised fresh waters, and so there was no need at that stage for any waterproofing mechanism. Berrill[22] also associated the acquisition of bone with the adoption of life in fresh waters, but contended that, because of the excess phosphate which these animals would have met in rivers, some means of excreting this substance must have been necessary. He imagined that for some reason the kidneys at this stage of evolution would not have been capable of dealing with such excess phosphate, and therefore the ostracoderms would have emulated the arthropods by laying down their excretory products as an exoskeleton. Not only is there nothing on which to base this view of the powers of the kidney, but neither is there any evidence that the phosphate content of fresh water differs greatly from that of the sea. At the present time there is a large concentration of phosphates at the mouths of major rivers but this is in large measure due to urban effluent—hardly to be expected some 500 million years ago! In fact there is no evidence that there was an appreciable difference in phosphate content between salt and fresh waters at the time of the first vertebrates.

As the ostracoderms had acquired their armour before they left the sea, Berrill's arguments also are invalidated. Nevertheless, he did go on to make a further suggestion, namely that in the course of evolution the early vertebrates came to utilise their excess phosphate as a means of energy transfer in their normal metabolism. In fact there seems no reason at all for this use of phosphate not to be absolutely basic to the vertebrates. Calcium phosphate may have been primarily laid down as a chemical store. Pautard,[157,158] on the basis of his work on certain protozoans, has suggested that a conveniently accessible phosphate store is likely to have been needed by any organism with much muscular activity; and from this it seems reasonable to postulate that bone evolved initially as such a store. There is an abundance of calcium in the sea and thus calcium phosphate is a convenient method of storing phosphate. Only very much later in evolution, when the vertebrates had gained the land, did the calcium become the most important component in bone. In the early vertebrates it was the phosphate that was of prime importance. Pautard believed that it was probably the shortage of phosphorus in ancient seas that encouraged the emergence of animals capable of forming their own store of calcium phosphate.

It is generally recognised that, although phosphates are not abundant in the seas at the present time, nevertheless there seems to be sufficient to support a considerable amount of life. Clearly the matter is rather more complex than might at first be imagined. There is a seasonal phosphate cycle in the sea. It begins in the spring with a redistribution of the free phosphates after the waters have been stirred up by the winter gales. The free phosphates reach their maximum in the winter. It should be remembered, however, that they are in a form readily assimilable not by animals, but only by plants. During spring and summer as the days lengthen, the amount of sunlight increases and phytoplankton multiplies in the upper zone of the sea using up all the available phosphates in that zone. Since the waters are fairly calm during the summer, the salts removed from the surface waters are not replenished from below. The phosphates are therefore locked in the phytoplankton, which either dies and sinks to the bottom or is eaten by other animals. Whichever happens, there is a continual loss of phosphates from the upper to the lower layers. However, these are now in a form in which they can be utilised by bottom-living animals, such as the detritus-feeding ostracoderms. Towards the end of the summer, when there are no longer any phosphates left in the upper waters, the plankton dies off. Frequently, with autumnal gales, the upper layers are replenished from below and as there is still a reasonable amount of sunlight, there occurs a short burst of planktonic reproduction. Insufficient sunlight eventually curtails this activity and the supply of assimilable phosphates for the bottom-dwellers ceases completely. Although the waters are stirred up by the winter gales, the free phosphates cannot be used by the animals present, and so, despite a maximum of such salts in the water, the animals in fact suffer a shortage. There is therefore a considerable advantage to be gained if a phosphate store can be built up in times of abundance to counteract the seasonal dearth.[220] This is particularly the case in animals that live for several years, as did the ostracoderms, and also for animals of any appreciable size (i.e. more than 3 or 4 cm long). In spite of the obvious value of such a chemical store, the actual amounts involved need not have been very great, in view of the comparatively low metabolic rate of cold-blooded animals. Furthermore, phosphate storage does not appear to be associated with any significant changes in the general pattern of marine life or in the chemistry of the sea. All the available geological evidence shows that there have been no essential changes in the bottom and tidal conditions in the 500 million years since the first records of the vertebrates. It seems that conditions in the sea today are essentially similar to those existing at the time of the ostracoderms.

Bone seems, therefore, to have originated as a simple store of phosphates laid down in the skin of the earliest vertebrates. Once the ability to produce such a store had evolved, the calcium phosphate must rapidly have assumed the secondary function of a protective armour. Although its flexibility and strength might suggest that its initial function was supportive, these properties are merely fortuitous. Not until considerably later in evolution did bone come to replace the cartilaginous endoskeleton and take on the supporting role for which it is now most noted.

2 : Earliest Vertebrates

Remains of the earliest vertebrates consist of fragments of bony armour which are found in rocks of Ordovician age both in Russia and in the United States. They belong to primitive jawless vertebrates, the ostracoderms, which possessed a bony carapace in contrast to the naked living cyclostomes. However, this division of the jawless vertebrates, or agnathans, into the extinct and the extant is rather artificial and serves only to obscure a number of significant relationships.

These early agnathans had developed not only a bony armour but also an efficient nasal apparatus, eyes (including a pineal organ) and an advanced acousticolateralis system (i.e. organs of balance and hearing including a lateral-line system). All these features put the animals' vertebrate status beyond any doubt. However, since they had not evolved jaws, their mode of life must have been somewhat restricted, and with few exceptions the ostracoderms must have been mud-grubbers, finding their nutriment from organic debris on the sea-bed and later on the floors of lakes and rivers.

Heterostracans

The overall shape of these ostracoderms can be reconstructed from the plates of the carapace. It is apparent that the earliest group of agnathans, the heterostracans, had no lateral fins, and therefore little manoeuvrability in the three-dimensional medium in which they lived. Stability must, therefore, have been maintained by the overall shape of the body. In fact it seems difficult to envisage how any active control of the animals' movements was ever accomplished. The widest part of the heterostracan body was in the anterior region, which was covered by the carapace, the posterior trunk region being much narrower and also deeper. The animal was propelled forward by lateral movements of the tail. The greater width of the anterior part of the body gave a certain degree of stability by minimising any undue tendency to roll.

In the absence of paired fins an efficient means of controlling movement was necessary, particularly for raising the body from the bed of river, lake or sea. The ventral surface of the carapace was markedly convex, so that any forward movement of the body would automatically have lifted the animal free of the bottom. The swimming movement probably resembled a slow-motion bouncing flight of a finch. This unsophisticated type of movement was sufficient to move the animal from one patch of mud to another. The risk of being stuck in the mud was probably reduced by an occasional quick flick of the tail.

In spite of the seemingly limited potential of these animals, they underwent a remarkable radiation, and a surprisingly large number of unusual modifications of the basic form of the carapace evolved. The earliest heterostracans had a somewhat box-like shaped carapace composed of numerous small elements (Fig. 4a). The later Silurian cyathaspids were also small compact animals, some two or three inches long, with deep body-scales arranged on the segmental somatic musculature. The carapace had four main plates: a ventral, a dorsal and a pair of lateral branchials covering the gill apparatus (Fig. 4b). The latter opened to the exterior at the posterior edge of the carapace. The cyathaspids were also notable in having paired external nostrils (in front of the mouth on the ventral surface of the snout) thus demonstrating conclusively that, in common with the majority of the vertebrates, the heterostracans had paired nasal sacs. The only important exceptions are the cyclostomes and their ostracoderm relatives. This suggests that among the ostracoderms there were at least two fundamentally distinct groups of jawless vertebrates.

One group of agnathans, the thelodonts, did not have a proper carapace, but were covered by discrete dermal denticles. The gills had individual openings but Ritchie (personal communication) has demonstrated that these became concentrated into essentially the heterostracan arrangement.

The major radiation of the heterostracans occurred in the Devonian period. Dominating the Lower Devonian, the pteraspids had developed long snouts, sharp dorsal spines and lateral cornual plates acting as stabilisers (Fig. 4f). The evolution of the pteraspids seems to have taken two major routes, one leading to the blade-snouted forms such as *Rhinopteraspis* and *Althaspis*, and a separate line of squat blunt-snouted forms such as *Europrotaspis*. Quite independent evolutionary lineages led to both of these two major types of specialisation. A study of the growth of the ventral surface of the snout region reveals that the blade-snouted condition was achieved by two quite distinct routes.[215]

The most peculiar pteraspid was the surface-feeding *Doryaspis* with its pair of scimitar shaped cornual plates and long narrow snout formed

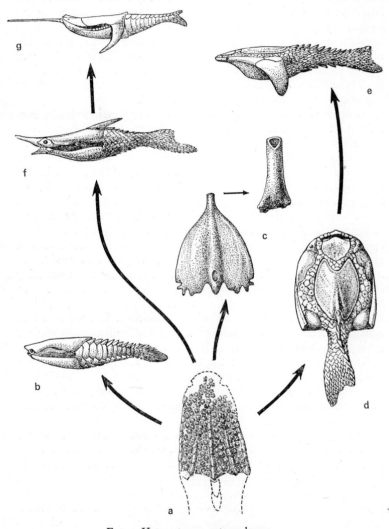

FIG. 4. Heterostracan ostracoderms

a. *Astraspis* (Ordovician); b. Cyathaspid (Silurian–Devonian); c. *Eglon-aspis* showing tubular mouth (Devonian); d. *Drepanaspis* (Lower Devonian); e. *Pycnosteus* (Middle Devonian); f. *Pteraspis* showing oral plates splayed out to form scoop (Lower Devonian); *Doryaspis* (Lower Devonian). (after Obruchev and Halstead Tarlo).

from one of the ventral plates of the armour, probably a specialised mouth plate (Fig. 4g).[142] The rostral plate which normally forms the projecting part of the carapace was, in this animal, a trap-door acting as a scoop for particles at the surface of the water.

The blind *Eglonaspis* represented another unique extreme of heterostracan specialisation (Fig. 4c).[142] The mouth was situated at the end of a long blunt tube, and presumably this genus was a mud burrower or at least lived in very turbid water.

Most of the heterostracans were comparatively small in size, the only exceptions being some of the long-snouted pteraspids and the psammosteids which are reputed to have reached six feet in length. The end of the Lower Devonian times marked the virtual eclipse of this once dominant group, except, however, for the psammosteids, which then began a minor evolutionary radiation of their own. In this group the ventral plates were sharply convex, the mouth on the dorsal surface, and the branchial plates formed wide lateral extensions to the carapace which Obruchev[140] believed enabled the animals to hold against the running waters of rivers. He suggested that the animals were able to feed passively by resting on the river bed, facing upstream with their heads on the bottom and their tails projecting into the water at an acute angle, while the branchial plates served to anchor the body. The extensive wear on the ventral surface of the carapace, however, would seem to militate against this interpretation of the feeding position and indicate that the animals lay flat on the bottom and not at an acute angle. The deep ventral carapace presumably must have housed an efficient pumping mechanism. It is inconceivable that a six foot long microphagous animal could have provided the necessary currents for ingesting sufficient food, solely by ciliary action.

One of the more unusual of the psammosteids, *Pycnosteus*, had branchial plates with a concave antero-lateral margin with a narrow zone of wear on both the ventral and dorsal surfaces (Fig. 4e). Attempts to orientate this plate to explain this pattern of abrasion have proved impossible. Currey[221] has postulated that the branchials were worn as the animal pushed its way through water-weeds dislodging the small invertebrates on which it fed.

With increasing size the area and amount of wear on the dermal plates of the psammosteids would also have increased by a factor equal to the square of the linear increment. It follows that, in order to minimise this wear, the area in contact with the river bottom should be reduced as far as possible. This has proved to be the case in the three known lineages where a progressive narrowing of the ventral median plates has occurred.[218] The extreme of this trend is seen in *Pycnosteus* where two sled-like runners were produced.[143] A com-

c

parable, albeit more delicate, set of runners is formed in *Obruchevia* by the branchial plates which were turned ventrally at an angle of 90°.[222] Despite the evolution of so many bizarre forms, the heterostracans never developed paired fins, although the Upper Devonian *Psammosteus* could, to some extent, move its branchial plates.[222]

Cephalaspids

Paired fins were, however, evolved by the osteostracans or cephalaspids. This group showed an evolution towards a more efficient benthonic mode of life, during late Silurian and early Devonian times. The early forms had a carapace not unlike that of a cyathaspid heterostracan, as the ventral profile was convex (Fig. 5a). There were clearly no lateral projections to act as stabilisers and the method of swimming must have been essentially similar to that of the heterostracans. In the later cephalaspids the ventral surface was flat and the dorsal one markedly convex, implying a benthonic mode of life. They must also have acquired some means of ensuring that any movement of the tail did not simply drive them deeper into the mud. The history of the cephalaspids illustrates exactly how this particular problem was overcome and their overall efficiency and manoeuvrability improved. The posterior part of the carapace was somewhat reduced, so increasing the mobile, and hence propulsive part, of the animal. At the same time the cephalaspids developed, in conjunction with a heterocercal tail, lateral pectoral flaps which would have aided in the maintenance of stability. Heintz[78] has shown this tail to be unique among the vertebrates in having horizontal tail flaps. In the ateleaspids the posterior part of the carapace was reduced and the posterolateral corners of the armour were produced into thin pectoral flaps (Fig. 5c–e). The leading edges of these were highly vulnerable, and thus the marginal elements of the armour tended to be more massive in this region. Furthermore, the part of the carapace immediately in front of the flaps became drawn out into a sharp point, again simply to protect the leading edge of the pectoral flap. This produced the characteristic cephalaspid spine or cornua (Fig. 5b, f). The typical cephalaspid, therefore, is characterised by the shortness of its carapace and by the marked development of cornua and pectoral flaps.

As befits an animal adapted for life on the bottom, the eyes of the cephalaspids were situated on the top of the head, the mouth was ventral and the floor of the buccal cavity flexible. The individual openings of the separate gill pouches lay along the lateral margins of the buccal cavity. The third eye, the pineal, probably functioned as a light-sensitive organ in these animals, as it was not covered by the dorsal dermal armour as in the heterostracans, but opened between the eyes. The fourth opening in the dorsal armour of the head (the entry to the naso-hypophyseal sac) lay anterior to the pineal, a position it occupies in the living lampreys or petromyzonid cyclostomes. Indeed it was from such anatomical details that Stensiö[197] was able to establish conclusively that the cephalaspids were closely related to the

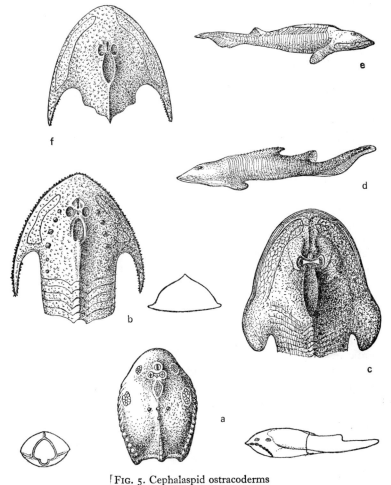

ⁱFIG. 5. Cephalaspid ostracoderms

a. *Tremataspis* (Silurian); b. *Thyestes* (Silurian); c, d. *Aceraspis* (Silurian–Devonian); e. *Hemicyclaspis* (Silurian–Devonian); f. *Cephalaspis* (Devonian). (after Heintz, Obruchev and Stensiö).

lampreys. As well as these structures, the cephalaspids are noted for their possession of so-called 'electric fields'. These were in fact extensions of the labyrinth of the ear and must have been filled by endolymph. The small polygonal plates of the lateral and dorsal sensory fields were movable and any vibrations impinging upon them could have been transmitted to the brain. Clearly there was no room for an electric organ of any known kind and no evidence for Stensiö's suggestion that the large canals contained important motor nerves.[197,199,204]

Anaspids

The anaspids, the third major group of ostracoderms, were closely related to the cephalaspids despite a quite dissimilar appearance.[105] The body shape was much more fish-like, indicating a more active mode of life. The head was covered by numerous small plates and, as with the cephalaspids, the gill pouches had separate openings (Fig. 6c, d). If the disposition of their openings is any guide, the gill pouches were all compressed into an oblique row. The buccal area appears to have been flexible and presumably housed a velar pumping organ. The tail in the anaspids was hypocercal and this was believed to be because, like the heteostracans, they had no paired fins; recently, however, Ritchie[168] has demonstrated that this group did possess the unusual combination of both paired fins and hypocercal tail. Although the anaspids were technically agnathan, the mouth in some genera was bordered by strong plates of dermal armour which probably had a function analogous to that of jaws and teeth. Stensiö[199] inferred that one of these plates, which appeared to have migrated onto the floor of the mouth, functioned as a support for a rasping tongue; but Ritchie[168] has confirmed Kiaer's[105] opinion that the bone in question had in fact been displaced from its original position at the lower border of the mouth.

The possession of a hypocercal tail together with paired fins is indicative of a surface feeder, and this combination is seen in an extreme form in the flying fish of the modern oceans.

The anaspids are clearly in most respects closer to the living cyclostomes than any other ostracoderms, and several authors have suggested that the origin of the modern agnathans is to be sought amongst them. Unfortunately, Strahan[205] has shown (in studying both the living and fossil agnathans, by plotting their developmental stages on Cartesian co-ordinates) that it is not possible to derive the modern lampreys, let alone the hagfishes, from the anaspids. They were already too specialised in the concentration of their branchial apparatus.

However, although this evidently applies to the typical anaspids, this is not the case for the first and most primitive of the group

Jamoytius (Fig. 6a, b). This genus was believed by Stensiö[199] to be an anaspid, and I[213] was able to confirm this interpretation. Subsequently Ritchie,[167] from further specimens, showed that the branchial region was not concentrated and, furthermore, that it had a cartilaginous supporting basket comparable to that known in the lamprey.[169] Also

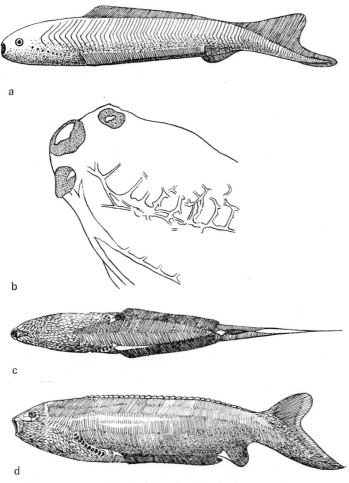

a

b

c

d

FIG. 6. Anaspid ostracoderms

a, b. *Jamoytius* (Silurian). a. Restoration; b. Head region to show branchial basket, eyes and mouth, c, d. *Pharyngolepis* (Silurian). c. ventral view showing lateral fins; d. lateral view. (after Ritchie.)

of interest is the finding that the mouth was perfectly circular, as in the cyclostomes.

Carapaces covered with clearly defined round perforations have been found in the same deposits as *Jamoytius* and have been identified as those of eurypterids—giant freshwater scorpions. The diameters of the perforations are of a size consistent with that of the mouth of *Jamoytius*,[169] so rather than the expected pattern of scorpions preying on ostracoderms, the reverse seems to have been the case!

The living cyclostomes are worm-like in appearance and covered by skin, their ancestors the anaspids were fish-shaped and covered with dermal armour. These changes can best be attributed to alterations in the behaviour of the two groups. The ostracoderms were in general semi-sessile bottom feeders, needing only to maintain their position without undue drifting or sinking into the mud. In contrast, the lampreys are external parasites of larger vertebrates, fixing themselves by their sucker mouth and using their rasping tongue and horny teeth to remove the skin of the host and gain access to the nutrient body fluid—a tendency first demonstrated by *Jamoytius*! The only movement required of the lamprey is in transference from one host to another. Simple sinuous movements suffice for this latter operation.

The other living cyclostomes, the hagfish, like the ostracoderms, are bottom feeders; but instead of lying on the surface of the sediment, they burrow into it—an essentially worm-like habit. Despite their resemblances to the lampreys, which are known to have evolved from the Silurian anaspids, the origin of the hagfish is, as yet, quite unknown.

The majority of the agnathans, being jawless, were obliged to be detrital feeders or, more crudely, mud-grubbers. This being so, they were clearly vulnerable to competition from the more advanced carnivorous jawed vertebrates. Only two viable ecological niches were available for such animals: one, that of general scavengers (in which they were fairly safe, spending much of their time buried in sediment), the other, that of ectoparasites. It is just these two modes of life that characterise the two surviving groups of agnathans. In spite of the seemingly limited potential of the first jawless vertebrates, nevertheless, within them can be found the blueprint for all the later major advances in vertebrate history.

3 : Skin, Dentine and Teeth

The classification of the heterostracans is based on the pattern and number of the dermal plates forming the carapace. In some, the carapace consists of only two or four major plates, whilst in others it is formed from small polygonal plates or tesserae. There has been considerable argument as to which of these was the more primitive. Perhaps because the carapace formed of a few plates appeared simple, the view became established that the simplest-looking type of carapace was the more primitive and that the major evolutionary trend was towards the breakup of such a carapace into smaller units. The latter type was thought more advantageous as it was believed to have conferred greater flexibility on the animal. However, when the specimens are examined in the sequence in which they make their appearance in the fossil record, it becomes apparent that the supposedly most advanced occur first and are followed much later in time by the so-called primitive forms. In addition to this, from superficial examination of the armour it is possible to study its growth, by virtue of the fact that the outermost layer was composed of dentine, the major constituent of teeth. Dentine is a calcified tissue, its formative cells, odontoblasts, laying down an organic matrix in which calcium salts are deposited. The deposition of the collagenous matrix begins at the surface, more being laid down and progressively calcified as the cells retreat inwards. This means that, once formed, the tissue cannot be altered except by wear or partial resorption. It follows that by analysing the patterns of dentine tubercles or ridges the growth stages of the animals concerned can be traced. When this is done, it becomes evident that the complexity of the earliest forms is more apparent than real.

The simplest method of forming plates of dermal armour is to begin with a series of isolated elements scattered in the skin (Fig. 7a). These act as foci around which further concentric growth can take place until the animal reaches its definitive size and these separate areas of armour meet to produce a terrazzo of polygonal plates or tesserae

(Fig. 7b, c). This method of producing a carapace is, obviously, much simpler than forming large plates *de novo* once the animal reaches maturity. Although the latter may appear simple, it clearly involves a much higher degree of physiological adaptation than would initially appear.

Development of Patterns of Dermal Armour

In spite of the fact that the pattern of plates in the early vertebrates was always in the form of a terrazzo, this particular system was gradually eliminated in favour of a more rigidly organised arrangement of large plates. The stages in the gradual fusion and elimination of tesserae have been carefully documented.[217] The cyathaspid *Tolypelepis* has a large dorsal shield formed from the fusion of numerous tesserae which show that they grew by the addition of dentine ridges at either side of the initial one.[141] Later cyathaspids show two generations of ridges only, whilst the more advanced reveal little evidence of the prior existence of tesserae. In these latter cases the armour did not develop until the individuals reached their definitive size; presumably until this stage they must have been quite naked. In the unusual genus *Corvaspis* the tesserae were eliminated in a quite different manner (Fig. 7d–i).[214] They appeared simultaneously just before the animal reached its definitive size, and then extra tubercles developed in narrow zones between them. Around the large plates that were formed by the fusion of these tesserae there occurred a narrow zone of concentric growth. The elimination of tesserae proceeded as follows: the individual tesserae became separated merely by a narrow groove, then some of them became confluent; eventually there was hardly any sign at all of the original tesserae apart from the occasional transverse groove and irregularity of the dentine ridges.

From the fusion and elimination of the primitive tesserae an organised system of large plates was built up. These plates then appeared earlier and earlier during the life history of the individuals, so that they began as small primordia around which concentric zones of growth took place. Indeed it was comparable to the situation found in the primitive areally growing tesserae of the very earliest vertebrates, except that now this same arrangement was more highly organised. With this type of growth it became possible for extensions to the carapace to be developed, since they would be assured of constant support during their early growth stages. The production of laterally projecting sheets of bone as stabilising organs eventually led, in at least one group, to the formation of movable 'paired appendages'.[221]

One of the problems with regard to the evolution of the heterostracan

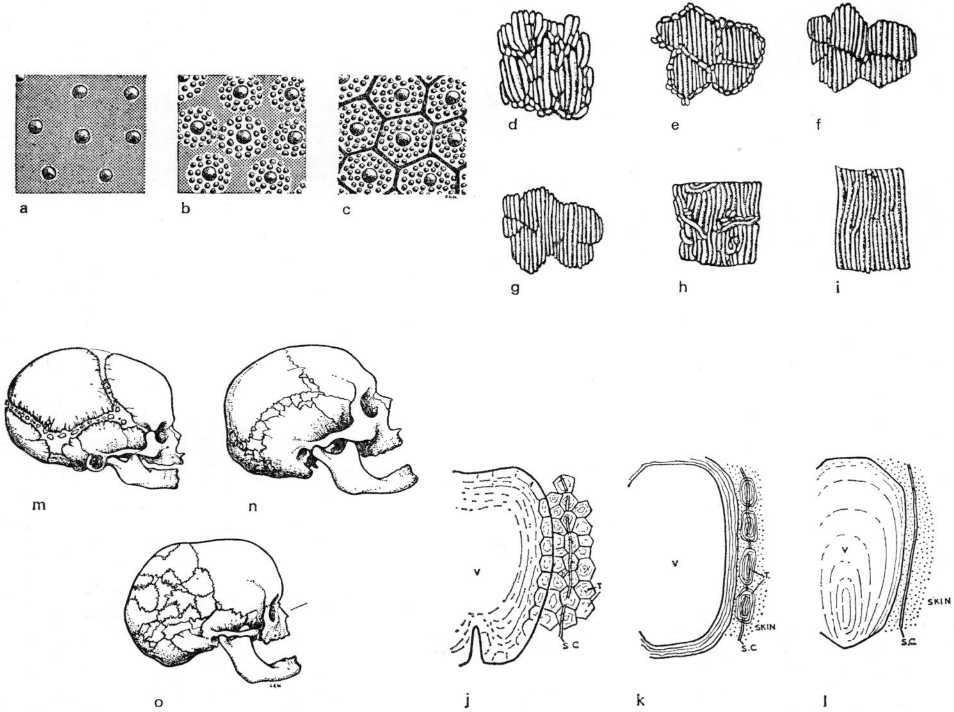

FIG. 7. Development of tesserae a. isolated tubercles evenly distributed in skin; b. concentric rings of tubercles present around primordia, with surviving areas of naked skin; c. fully formed terrazzo of abutting tesserae; d-i. Elimination of tesserae. d. primitive cyclomorial tesserae; e. synchronomorial tesserae separated by narrow zone of cyclomorial growth; f. synchronomorial tesserae separated by fine grooves; g. partially fused synchronomorial tesserae; h. synchronomorial region with irregularities indicating former existence of synchronomorial tesserae; i. synchronomorial unit with no sign of former tesserae; j-l. Early growth stages to illustrate gradual reduction (j-l) or development (l-j) of fields of tesserae: j. psammosteid; k. traquairaspidid; l. pteraspidid; m-o. *Skull of Homo sapiens* L.; m. newborn child showing developing ossification centres between main skull bones; n. adult condition to show appearance of Wormian bones; o. adult with parietals composed of small bones. (from Halstead Tarlo).

carapace has been the fact that the later forms, the psammosteids, possessed large median plates with a superficial ornamentation of polygonal tesserae showing concentric growth patterns. Indeed, the psammosteids are characterised by the possession of a narrow zone of tesserae situated between the median plates and those of the lateral margins. These tesserae appear to have spread over the greater part of the median areas of the carapace, although beneath them there grew the normal large median plates, so that the basic pattern of plates was not in fact lost—the tesserae simply redeveloped. For several years I have argued that the fields of tesserae of the psammosteids were surviving remnants from the tessellated carapace of the earliest vertebrates.[218] In fact, they were part of the original primitive arrangement that had never been lost. I suggested that the psammosteids by the further reduction of these fields gave rise to the traquairaspids in which there was a single row of small units around the median plates, which, however, later in development became incorporated in the main plates (Fig. 7j–l). Finally, by the complete loss of the tesserae, the carapace of the pteraspids could have been developed. The absence of fields of tesserae in the early developmental stages of the primitive psammosteid *Drepanaspis*, as well as in *Guerichosteus*, seems to militate against this interpretation. Obruchev's[139] proposition that the tesserae were lost and subsequently re-evolved might appear unlikely, if only on the grounds of economy of hypotheses; however, there now seems every justification for accepting this view.[245]

The facility with which the skin produces dermal skeletal structures is well known throughout the vertebrates, and they generally occur as isolated small discrete units. For example, between the major bones of the human skull small ossicles, the Wormian bones of the adult, may form. In some instances instead of discrete bones such as parietals this part of the skull may be made up of a large number of separate units (Fig. 7m–o). The development of the psammosteid fields of tesserae are in fact believed by Obruchev[139] to have come about in a comparable manner. Whether or not this was the case, there can be little doubt that the potential for the development of such units exists and can be easily exercised. Whimster[246,247] as a result of his studies of the skin of amphibians and reptiles, as well as of the nature of dermal diseases, has suggested that there is an inherent mosaic pattern in all vertebrate skin. This is not immediately evident in man, but in pathological conditions the underlying fundamental pattern is brought to light. Whatever the nature of the particular skin disease, whether it is characterised by spots or pustules, the lesions develop in the same way: they begin as well separated individual pustules, around which more form to become confluent eventually. It is clear that there is a basic tessellated pattern, such as was found in the earliest vertebrates. Whimster[246,247] believes that this pattern may be determined by the nervous system. The crux of the matter is to find a likely reason for the production of isolated and fairly evenly spaced foci, whether of epidermal keratinous or mesodermal bony structures. Once these are present, given areal growth around them, a tessellated pattern must automatically follow, just as the packing of cylindrical cells in a honeycomb produces the characteristic hexagonal pattern. It is well known that although a tessellated pattern can be produced by packing, it can also be the result of the breakup of a homogeneous substance. This is classically seen in Bénard cells and also in fermenting wine and in the soap-bubble froth at the top of a wash-tub. Turing[234] has shown that the distribution of chemical substances in a tissue cannot be entirely uniform, and in consequence the equivalent of standing waves of particular substances will build up to give evenly distributed high spots of concentration. It is easy to envisage how the initial foci required to set the entire tessellated pattern into operation could have been initiated in this way. In any event, it seems likely that the origin of this pattern in skin is due in the final analysis to simple physico-chemical factors. Although this basic pattern becomes obscured during the course of evolution and seems in some cases to be under nervous control, the explanation of its ultimate origin is not affected. The fact that it can readily be redeveloped in every group of vertebrates is certainly indicative of its being a fundamental property of vertebrate skin.[224]

Dentine—a Primitive Skin

Since the bony armour forming the outer covering of the animal was the main barrier between it and the environment, it can justifiably be regarded as skin, particularly the dentine forming the superficial part of the armour (Fig. 8a, b). In the heterostracans the dentine was not covered by enamel, as it is in the teeth of the higher vertebrates, and although it was initially subepidermal it ultimately became exposed, as is evidenced by the faint abrasion which occurred over the entire surface of the animals. The covering tissue of an animal must be sensitive for it to be viable. As my wife[208] has suggested, the still-surviving system of radiating tubules, which extend in teeth from the pulp cavity to the outer surface of the dentine and are the pathway for sensation, may well be connected with the original skinlike role of this tissue in the earliest vertebrates.

However, it is not enough for an outer covering to be merely sensitive; it must also be capable of responding to damage of either a slight or a serious nature. It follows that the dentine in the heterostracans

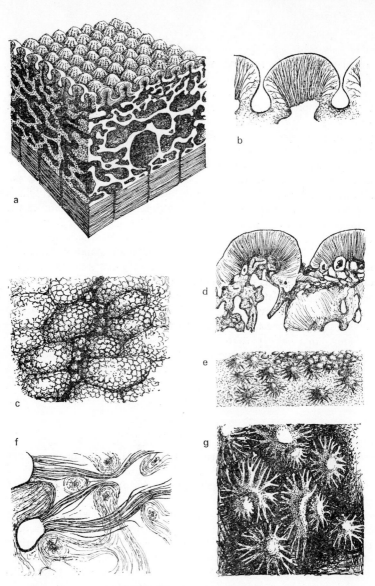

FIG. 8. Heterostracan dentine

a. Block diagram showing basal lamellar aspidin, spongy aspidin and superficial dentine tubercles; b. detail of dentine tubercle illustrating lateral and terminal branches of tubules; c. break in armour healed by new tubercles; d. second generation tubercles positioned on top of earlier, the latter showing evidence of resorption, trabeculae of aspidin developing; e. new tubercles spreading over old tuberculated surface; f. pleromic (infilling) dentine filling vascular spaces in spongy aspidin; g. new developing tubercles situated in resorption cavities on old tubercles.

must have possessed the property of repair. Where some individuals had suffered the attention of predators and had parts of their carapace bitten off, especially the edges of laterally projecting plates, the wound was healed over by a new layer of dentine tubercles.[222] Presumably the epidermal tissue at the margin of the bite would have spread across the damaged region and the mesodermal tissue would have become organised beneath it and produced a new generation of tubercles (Fig. 8c). This production of new dentine units took place wherever parts of the armour were severely damaged or lost. Where only slight damage or some kind of intermittent irritation or abrasion occurred, as at the posterior tips of psammosteid branchials, a different pattern of regeneration is found. Apparently the epidermal tissue, forming a network around the bases of the tubercles, was stimulated so that it proliferated over the irritated surface. Beneath it new dentine tubercles developed; but, instead of simply replacing the worn units, they were positioned on top of the old surface (Fig. 8d, e). The placing of new generations on top of the old seems quite anomalous but there can be no doubt that such was indeed the case.[92] Occasionally worn tubercles are found with new unworn ones on top of them, sometimes tubercles of the older generation show marked resorption cavities in their sides with new developing tubercles situated in these corrie-like hollows (Fig. 8g).[210] Since there is no doubt as to the relative positions of the successive generations of dentine tubercles or of their homology with teeth, this apparent reversal of the successional sequence needs some explanation. New generations of teeth almost always erupt from below, resorbing the roots and never the summits of the first generation. My wife has pointed out that from an examination of the embryological development of human and other vertebrate dentitions, it becomes evident that this seemingly fundamental difference is more apparent than real.[209] In the early stages, the germ of the second generation tooth is positioned above and to the side of the first—much the same spatial arrangement as is found in the heterostracan tubercles. It is only later in development that the relative positions of the two teeth change and the new tooth comes to lie beneath the one it will eventually replace. Only by such a rearrangement through differential growth could a continually functioning dentition be assured at all times. This is clearly necessary once the tubercles take on the function of teeth; indeed, teeth can be considered as the last vestiges of dermal armour, which have survived only in the region of the mouth and then only because they were able to subserve an entirely new function. The ability of the skin of the heterostracans to produce new generations of dentine tubercles was initially a healing or protective mechanism developed as a response to external irritation of some kind. With the change from tubercle to tooth, this same mechanism survived, although it became more highly organised and controlled. From an examination of the behaviour of heterostracan skin, it is possible to see how the entire system of tooth replacement must have arisen.

However, although the production of secondary tubercles as a response to abrasion must have been of considerable value, it was not without its disadvantages. During the period when new growth was occurring, it would have been necessary for the animal to enter a period of enforced inactivity, since any undue movement would have disrupted the reparative processes. This would have been a serious problem only with the larger forms, such as the psammosteids, which would be likely to suffer considerable abrasion as they moved their large bulks over the sandy and gravelly river beds. In these animals, when abrasion of the tubercles began, the epidermal tissue and the underlying mesenchymal cells, which were situated between the tubercles, induced the formation of odontoblasts, which then started producing the organic matrix of dentine. As they retreated, dentine gradually filled in the anastomosing spaces of the spongy bone-like tissue which underlay the dentine ornamentation (Fig. 8f). This infilling dentine, for which my wife has coined the term 'pleromic dentine', filled in the space in the armour in order to strengthen those parts subject to excessive wear.[226] In this way the strengthening was able to keep pace with the wear, and, as the thickening took place internally, there was no need for any periods of enforced immobility. The nature of pleromic dentine was somewhat similar to the secondary dentine found in teeth, in that there were few tubules, the greater part of the infilling being devoid of them. Those that were present, however, were extremely long and wound their way through the spongy tissue, now made quite solid.

Usually, damaged tubercles were not repaired but allowed to wear away. However, in the laterally projecting plates, where the tubercles were being worn away from the sides, as pleromic dentine invaded the floor of the pulp cavity some of the pulpal cells seem to have been activated, and dentine tubules from the tubercle itself can be seen to have run in parallel with the migrating odontoblasts in their retreat from the surface of severe abrasion.[221,222]

Normally, secondary dentine in teeth is confined to the region of the pulp. A regular type of secondary dentine is formed in response to the normal wear on teeth, although attrition is less often seen in modern man than in his more recent ancestors, a change that can in large measure be attributed to diet. This type of slowly formed dentine is not dissimilar from the normal, but where more rapid destruction of tooth substance occurs, as in the spread of dental decay, the secondary dentine then formed is comparable to pleromic dentine in its general organisation. This reaction to severe abrasion is exactly the same as that of the heterostracans living in rivers hundreds of millions of years ago. In fact the healing mechanism of these animals still survives, admittedly in a reduced form, in ourselves. Our teeth are to a limited extent capable of repair, although unfortunately often too little and too late! Study of the dentine in heterostracan armour gives new insight into its intrinsic properties. Such studies not only demonstrate the fundamental structure of dentine but in addition elucidate a number of basic processes which otherwise would be hard to explain.

The Origin of Tooth Cusps

Since it is evident that the dentine tubercles of the heterostracans are homologous with the teeth of the higher vertebrates as well as with the scales of fish, or at least the superficial dentine parts, it can therefore be expected that other features characteristic of teeth would have their origins in the armour of ancient aquatic vertebrates. Teeth are frequently homologised with the placoid scales of the sharks and there can be no question that the teeth of sharks are homologous with the scales of the same animals. This type of sharp high-crowned scale can very easily be transformed into the simple conical tooth found in fish, amphibians and reptiles. From this simple beginning all the complex teeth of the higher vertebrates with their complicated cuspal patterns are ultimately to be derived.

The placoid scale is considered by Romer[10,12] and J. Z. Young[16] to represent the final stage in the breakdown of the dermal armour of the earliest vertebrates; but in spite of these opinions it is generally accepted that the placoid scale is a primitive structure, and that this is also true of the simple conical tooth. However, examination of the earliest shark scales shows that they were extremely complex and that true placoid scales did not appear in the fossil record until many million years later. Stensiö[201,202] and Ørvig[147] have demonstrated that, far from being a primitive structure, the placoid scale is the end result of a long evolutionary history; a trend in fact towards an apparent simplification. This is another cautionary tale to warn against assuming that an object is primitive because it appears simple.

Stensiö and Ørvig have presented abundant evidence to establish that the placoid scale resulted from the progressive fusion of small elements to form larger ones. Indeed, the history of the fusion and consequent elimination of the minor units is an almost exact repetition of what occurred in the evolution of the heterostracan armour. Similarly the resultant major units retained the potential to redevelop their minor constituents at any stage. At the present time this previous history is not reflected in the embryology of the placoid scale; only the fossil record reveals the earlier course of events. The observations of Stensiö and Ørvig have made it possible to suggest the way in which tooth cusps may have originated. Bolk and others successfully advocated that the complex pattern of tooth cusps which characterise the mammalian molar was derived from the fusion of several germs of single conical teeth. The coalescence of primitive conical teeth was believed to be associated with shortening of the jaws, which would have crowded the teeth together unduly. Bolk's famous 'Dimer Theory' postulated the fusion of the tooth germs of two triconodont teeth. This theory did not, however, explain the origin of the triconodont tooth itself. The Cope-Osborn tritubercular theory, as modified by Gregory, discussed the origin of the tribosphenic molar in the light of observations on fossil material. These authors did not postulate the fusion of tooth germs to explain the origins of the cusps they discussed, but suggested that all subsidiary cusps developed from the margins of the base or slopes of the first original conical tooth. Recently Mills[127] has provided a functional explanation for their evolution. The theories that have been put forward in the past to explain the existence of cusps on teeth can be better understood in the context of the 'Lepidomorial Theory' of Stensiö and Ørvig, derived from their study of fossil shark scales.[147,201,202]

The above authors believed that in the earliest stage the skin was dotted with minute simple elements termed lepidomoria, each with a single vascular loop and simple pulp cavity (Fig. 9a). Frequently these simple units would become united at their bases, although their crowns would still remain separate (Fig. 9b). New units were then added, one at a time, with part of the wall of the crown of the earlier units forming the wall of the newer units (Fig. 9c). In this way further units were added to the earlier ones without the need to produce complete crowns. The next stage involved the contemporaneous formation and fusion of the lepidomoria before calcification, so that once hard tissue was laid down, it formed a continuous sheet over all the different constituent elements (Fig. 9d–f). This resulted in a complex pattern of shared pulp cavities, the only evidence for the original lepidomoria being in the form of its extensions and in the nature of the external ridges on the outer surface of the scale. This type of growth, in which the separate elements arise simultaneously, is termed *synchronomorial*, in contrast to *cyclomorial* growth, in which separate units are added on one at a time in a concentric manner. Once these small synchronomorial scales had evolved, they themselves formed centres of growth around which similar scales were added on cyclomorially (Fig. 9g). This resulted in the formation of extremely complex types of

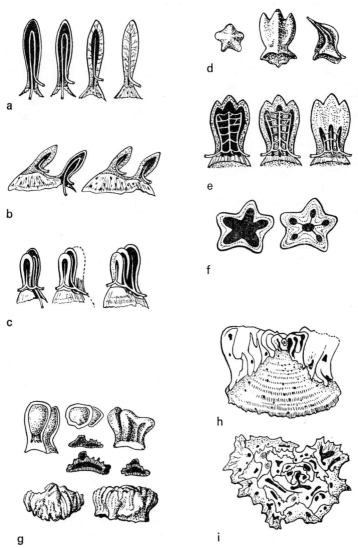

FIG. 9. Primitive shark scales illustrating the Lepidomorial Theory:
a. development of isolated lepidomorium; b. scale composed of two
lepidomoria with crowns separate; c. scale formed by adjoining lepidomoria with shared walls; d–f. Synchronomorial scale formed by fusion
of lepidomoria: d. external view; e. vertical section; f. horizontal section;
g. cyclomorial scales composed of synchronomorial units around a central
primordium; h–i. Complex scale formed by areal growth of synchronomorial units: h. vertical section; i. horizontal section. (after Stensiö).

scale. With further fusion in the concentric zones, a number of units became joined together to form large composite synchronomorial areas (Fig. 9h, i). Composite units could then arise simultaneously, so that complete rings would have been added onto the initial primordium. Indeed, such a state of affairs is to be found in the scales of modern bony fish with their concentric growth rings. However, the placoid scale represents an advance on this condition, since the adjoining rings have themselves arisen simultaneously until eventually the complete scale was formed as a single unit. The only evidence for the history of the placoid scale is to be found in the complex ramifications of the pulp cavity and the series of ridges and cusps on the outer surface of the scale or tooth.

The placoid scale, far from being a simple primitive structure, is, in fact, a highly specialised one, being considerably more advanced than the cyclomorial scale found in the bony fish. Moreover, since the conical tooth of the early vertebrates was clearly derived from a placoid-type scale, it too probably passed through the evolutionary stages outlined. If this is accepted, it becomes easy to envisage the way in which cusped teeth could have arisen. For instance, if the uncalcified primordium arose a little earlier in ontogeny than the surrounding rings or components or rings, these elements would be at different stages of growth and hence at different heights. When calcification took place in all the elements simultaneously, the tooth, instead of appearing as a simple cone would have a crown composed of cusps of various dimensions. By altering the order and timing of any of its component parts, any type of cusp pattern could be produced, although naturally, during embryological development, the various stages would not necessarily be apparent, the enamel organ merely coming to outline the final shape.

Teeth

Teeth can be considered as structures with almost unlimited potential as far as their outer form is concerned, so much so that in most vertebrates their form is more closely related to the animal's diet and mode of life than to its evolutionary lineage. Teeth are particularly subject to adaptation and it is not at all unusual to find that completely unrelated animals occupying identical ecological niches possess similar dentitions. Some of the most striking examples of this convergent evolution in tooth form can be found amongst the aquatic vertebrates. The walrus (an extant mammal), the placodonts and shastosaurid ichthyosaurs (both Triassic reptiles), the globident mosasaurs (giant Cretaceous lizards) as well as the teleost wolf-fish, the rays and the Port Jackson shark *Heterodontus*, all have rounded or flat tooth plates for crushing the shells of molluscs on which they feed. Similarly pike, gavials, the extinct marine crocodiles, the reptilian mesosaurs and plesiosaurs and the living cetaceans, such as the common dolphin, have homodont dentitions with large numbers of simple sharply pointed teeth for grasping the fish on which they prey. The chisel-like incisors typifying the rodents of today have also evolved in the lagomorphs the rabbits and hares, in a primate the aye-aye of Madagascar, as well as in the extinct typotheres of South America. In these animals they are permanently growing, but similarly shaped and functional teeth also occurred in the Triassic ictidosaurian mammal-like reptiles and in the Cretaceous true mammalian multituberculates.

A parallel, perhaps not so obvious, but in its own way just as striking, is the independent development from different elements of the dentition, of highly specialised teeth such as the carnassials, the shearing teeth of flesh-eating mammals. All living carnivores, such as dogs and cats have carnassials developed from the same teeth, the fourth upper premolar and the first lower molar. However, at the beginning of the Tertiary, some seventy million years ago, there were a number of archaic carnivorous mammals which are collectively known as creodonts, although they belong to two separate orders the Condylarthra and the Deltatheridia and not to the Carnivora. The cat-like creodonts had carnassials developed from the first upper molar and second lower but in the hyaena-like forms the second upper and third lower molars were the specialised teeth.

As well as such similarities in relation to individual teeth, occasionally dentitions appear quite anomalous in the particular animals in which they are found. The most dramatic example of this is a small ornithischian dinosaur from the Triassic of Lesotho recently described by Crompton and Charig.[45] This genus *Heterodontosaurus* was characterised by its 'mammalian' dentition as it was markedly heterodont with incisiform, caniniform and posterior grinding teeth (Fig. 36a, ii). Until this discovery it was always assumed that only the mammal-like reptiles and mammals could have had such a dentition.

Finally, if an animal takes to a diet requiring little chewing, such as ants or termites, then the teeth are reduced to simple pegs or lost altogether. There can be little doubt that the state of teeth in contemporary 'civilised' society, with the consequent demands laid on the dental profession, is a direct reflection of current feeding habits. It might be hoped that man will retain his teeth if only for cosmetic reasons, but Bystrow[1] had no hesitation in portraying the man of the future as toothless. It would surely be a pity, if at this stage in his evolution, man should lose one of his few direct inheritances from the heterostracans.

4 : Bone, Cartilage and the Skeleton

The dermal armour of the heterostracans did not consist only of dentine; the greater part of the carapace was formed of a three dimensional scaffolding of a bone-like tissue. The overall texture was the same as that of the cancellous bone of the skull, and it is evident that it must have formed in essentially the same way. In the loose connective tissue of the dermis, mesenchymal cells probably congregated in small clusters and extruded the collagenous matrix on which calcification was to take place. In this way small spicules of hard tissue could have been formed, and they would have enlarged by the addition of more calcified matrix. As this would have occurred in all directions away from the initial spicules, a series of radiating beams would have been constructed. These trabeculae would then have produced a three-dimensional scaffolding (Fig. 8a). Once such an initial scaffolding was erected, further hard tissue could be formed by appositional growth, enclosing the trabeculae in concentric layers of further hard tissue. In whatever plane this bone-like tissue from the heterostracans is sectioned, a system of trabeculae surrounded by concentric lamellae is found. Continued growth of lamellae will reduce the intertrabecular spaces until the tissue becomes progressively more compact. Indeed, the difference between cancellous and compact bone is simply one of degree. This method of laying down calcified tissue is the truly basic method of bone formation. The so-called cartilage bone and Haversian systems found in the vertebrate skeleton are much later evolutionary developments.

Aspidin—the Precursor of Bone

Although the general architecture of the bony armour is identical to that of bone, and although it seems to be formed in an identical way, there is controversy as to whether the hard tissue in the heterostracans should be designated bone. Gross[72] introduced the non-committal term

TISSUES		JAWLESS VERTEBRATES	PLACODERMS	CARTILAGINOUS FISH	BONY FISH	AMPHIBIANS	REPTILES	BIRDS	MAMMALS	MAN
ENAMEL							teeth lost by turtles etc.	teeth in earliest forms only	lost by some forms	
ENAMELOID — TOOTH						in larval form only				
ENAMELOID — SCALE ETC.					lost by most later forms					
DENTINE — TOOTH							teeth lost by turtles etc.	teeth in earliest forms only		
DENTINE — SCALE ETC.		lost in later forms			lost by most later groups					
ASPIDIN	primitive / advanced	lost in later forms	? BONE OF ATTACHMENT			? CEMENTUM / ? BONE OF ATTACHMENT		? CEMENTUM		? CEMENTUM
BONE — EXTERNAL		lost in later forms possessed by one group only		possessed by few early forms only		armour retained only by one group	armour retained by turtles etc. and crocs.		armour retained by some forms	
BONE — INTERNAL		small amount associated with cartilaginous endoskeleton in later forms	small amount associated with cartilaginous endoskeleton							
CARTILAGE						embryonic template small amount retained	embryonic template very small amount retained	embryonic template very small amount retained		

TABLE II. Distribution of Hard Tissues throughout the Vertebrates (From Tarlo and Tarlo, by permission of Editor of *Discovery*).

'aspidin' for this tissue, which is said to be characterised by the absence of bone-cell spaces. Generally speaking, the cells responsible for the production of the collagenous matrix become enclosed as it calcifies, surviving in lacunae connected by narrow channels or canaliculae. The position of such osteocytes can, therefore, easily be seen in fossil material. Bone, without included cells, is well known in several groups of modern bony fish, and Ørvig[148] has clearly documented the gradual evolution of this acellular type from the more normal cellular variety. This change was accomplished by the withdrawal of the cell bodies to the vascular canals. In view of the unequivocal evidence that the acellular bone of living bony fish was a secondary derivative of normal bone, Ørvig[147] and Stensiö[197] considered that the apparently acellular bone of the heterostracans must similarly be a comparable secondary development from true bone. Indeed, the concept became current that any hard tissue considered to be acellular cannot be primitive. Since aspidin did not possess normal bone cells, it was believed by Stensiö and Ørvig that it could have no bearing on the early development or possible origin of the tissue bone. However, since aspidin occurred in the earliest vertebrates, it would seem reasonable to consider, at least as a working hypothesis, the possibility that it might have been a primitively acellular tissue and therefore possibly the precursor of bone. Apart from one minute fragment, recorded by Ørvig,[152] there is not much indication of bone in the fossil record until some 100 million years after the first appearance of the heterostracans; which is a little surprising, as bone is as easily fossilised as aspidin.

The earliest aspidin was formed as simple trabeculae with the apposition of successive lamellae. The cells laying down the matrix, the 'aspidinoblasts' of Bystrow,[28] must have retreated inwards towards the vascular spaces as these became infilled. If, as has been suggested, aspidin began as a phosphate store, it might be expected that the mineral matter carried in the blood would be laid down fairly simply in consecutive layers. There is no sign of cell spaces or cell processes in this tissue, although occasionally fine tubules at right angles to the lamellae are present and these can perhaps be interpreted as marking the line of retreat of the aspidinoblasts, as was suggested by Obruchev.[138] In later examples of aspidin, a number of structures are visible, which take the form of innumerable randomly arranged spindle-shaped spaces. Although noted by many authors since the last century, they have been generally interpreted as marking the former position of bundles of collagen and in fact identified as *Sharpey's fibres*, regardless of their position of alignment. Sharpey's fibres are not components of internal systems, but are usually found anchoring one type of tissue to another; which is demonstrably not the case with the spindle-shaped structures in aspidin. It seems to me that these spaces mark the site of aspidin-forming cells which on producing the matrix were trapped within it, becoming aspidinocytes.[219] These cells can be directly compared to osteoblasts, which also begin life as simple spindle-shaped cells not unlike the fibroblasts from which, it may be supposed, they must ultimately be evolved. This more advanced type of aspidin appears to represent the beginning of the evolution of a cellular type of bone from an acellular.

Nonetheless, in examples of the latest heterostracans the tissue is much more highly organised, within the initial trabeculae the aspidino-cyte spaces are still randomly arranged; but in the concentric lamellae they are aligned parallel to the lamellae (Fig. 10a), an arrangement barely

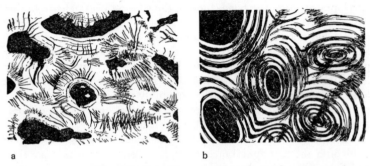

a   b

FIG. 10. a. aspidin showing cell spaces; b. advanced aspidin under polarised light to show black and white banding.

distinguishable from that of woven bone. A further similarity can be seen in the shape of the cell spaces of the trabeculae. As the lamellae were laid down, some of the aspidinocytes seem to have developed cytoplasmic extensions which became drawn out apparently in an attempt to maintain contact with the source of nutriment. Such a situation is found to occur with osteocytes enclosed in woven bone and also with the cementocytes of cementum. However, the elongation of the cell spaces appears to be connected only with initial trabeculae, as the aspidinoblasts responsible for the production of the matrix were not often trapped, but retreated as they formed the matrix.

Aspidin shows a gradual transition from an acellular calcified tissue to one, which, in all essentials, is hardly to be distinguished from bone. In any event, it seems reasonable to postulate that true bone could have arisen from an aspidin-type of tissue. Although the presence of cells is not in itself conclusive, it is important to attempt to trace the evolution of the organisation of the organic matrix. This task is not as difficult as might be imagined, since the crystallites of apatite are aligned parallel to the collagen fibrils. Therefore, by studying the alignment of the mineral components, the disposition of the underlying collagenous matrix can be inferred. This is done by examining sections under a polarising microscope. When the earliest aspidin is so examined, it can be seen that the collagen fibrils must have been arranged in parallel concentric layers. The organisation of the organic matrix was exactly the same as in dentine. However, when aspidin of later geological periods is studied, there is a broad black and white banding, indicating that the collagen fibrils were becoming organised into broad zones of different orientation. In the most advanced aspidin these zones are much narrower and are almost indistinguishable from modern bone (Fig. 10b).

It has been claimed that aspidin was not capable of being remodelled and so was basically different from bone. It has long been known that in mature heterostracans the plates fused at their edges, and when sectioned they showed no evidence of this fusion. In favourable sections examples of resorption can be seen, with the inference that aspidin-destroying cells or aspidinoclasts must have existed. Very occasionally examples of redeposition of aspidin can be found. Gross's[72] belief that aspidin was capable of remodelling, albeit in a rather rudimentary manner, has been vindicated.

Since it can be demonstrated that aspidin had all the essential attributes of bone, and since its evolution can be traced towards true bone and not in the opposite direction, it can no longer be considered as a secondary derivative of the latter. Aspidin clearly possessed cells which fulfilled the roles of osteoblasts, osteocytes and osteoclasts, and in the light of the above evidence it seems reasonable to consider it as a primitive type of bone, or at least its precursor.[219,220,221]

Ørvig[149,153] has suggested that dentine arose from a bone-like tissue, but it now seems far more likely that the most primitive type of vertebrate hard tissue was dentine-like and that bone evolved from it, as suggested by Warwick James.[89] The evolution of bone directly from aspidin is not established, but it is probable that it arose in the way outlined above. It is perfectly possible that bone evolved separately in different groups of vertebrates, but to date there is only the evidence of the evolution of aspidin to indicate the manner of its origin.

Cartilage *Versus* Bone

The evolution of such a hard skeletal tissue was quite unconnected with its later function as an internal support. This particular role was undertaken by cartilage. Ham[73] has suggested that bone evolved to replace calcified cartilage, and the view that bone and cartilage are intimately related, as far as evolution is concerned, has died hard. Authors have argued at length as to which came first, cartilage or bone, it being tacitly assumed that one or other must be primary. Reference is frequently made to the embryological development of the bony endoskeleton; which is supposed to indicate a compressed version of evolutionary history. Furthermore, the endoskeleton of primitive living vertebrates such as cyclostomes, sharks as well as primitive bony fish (e.g. sturgeon), is composed of cartilage. From the evidence of embryology and comparative anatomy it has been concluded that cartilage is primary and that bone must have subsequently evolved from it. On the other hand, palaeontologists point to the fossil record showing that all the primitive vertebrates were highly ossified, and that there was an evolutionary trend towards a reduction of bone resulting finally in a 'degenerate' cartilaginous skeleton.

Romer[174] has argued with great cogency that cartilage is an embryonic specialisation. He has pointed out that bone once formed is an unyielding substance and that, while this does not matter in dermal armour where bones float free in the skin, it would have serious consequences in the femur and other bones of the endoskeleton. Enlargement or elongation of bone results from the addition or accretion of new material at the surface; if, therefore, growth were to depend on this process, the arrangement of associated muscles, nerves and blood vessels would be continually disrupted. The formation of a cartilaginous template overcomes this difficulty. Cartilage has the remarkable property of growth by internal expansion, the cells divide and move apart as they produce more matrix. This mode of growth prevents disruption of its surface relations. Romer believed that cartilage originally was present only in the embryonic stages and that animals possessing a cartilaginous endoskeleton have simply retained a larval condition, another example of neoteny. It is true that during development cartilage is eminently suitable for forming an endoskeleton, but it is also perfectly adequate as an internal support for an aquatic vertebrate, as the success of the sharks testifies.

Although at the present time mesenchymal cells have the potential to produce fibrous tissue, cartilage or bone with equal facility, as far as evolution is concerned, there is no evidence whatsoever to suggest any direct connection between cartilage and bone. Bone evolved as a dermal structure, in all likelihood as a chemical store, but later became protective in function, whereas cartilage was primarily an internal supporting structure, to be eventually replaced by bone.

An apposite observation on this subject was made in the eighteenth century by John Hunter: 'Bone is not the original skeleton in any animal, but only of the adult; for in the first formation of any animal, which afterwards is to have bone, the skeleton is either membrane or cartilage, which is changed *for* bone, but not *into* bone.' This is evident when the stages in endochondral ossification are traced. The development of cartilage is well documented, although the reasons for the complex process still remain a mystery. Briefly, the chondroblasts lay down the intercellular matrix, which, although containing collagen fibres, is largely composed of chondromucin. Subsequently, the chondrocytes—as they have now become—hypertrophy or swell up. Phosphatases are secreted which induce calcification, and the cells become cut off from their sources of nutriment. The cells die and the matrix itself begins to disintegrate. In response to this, blood capillaries and osteoblasts invade the region, the latter beginning to produce bone, sometimes on remanent struts of calcified cartilage. The significant feature of this entire process is the destruction of the cartilage and its replacement by bone; in no sense is the cartilage changed into bone. It may well be that the cutting off of the source of nutriment leads to the replacement of the cartilaginous endoskeleton by bone.

The situation in the cephalaspids indicates a way in which this could have occurred. In the earlier genera the head skeleton was composed of cartilage; but, lining the major spaces in the head, around blood vessels and nerves, there was a thin layer of bone, an extension of the basal layer of the dermal armour.[56] In the later cephalaspids the entire internal skeleton of the headshield was composed of bone. It seems quite possible that with direct abutment of cartilage against bone, the point of contact would have been such that it could have sealed off the cartilage, which would then in all probability have died. This would have stimulated the production of more bone to replace the dead cartilage. In effect a chain reaction would have occurred, leading to a complete substitution of bone for cartilage. It is this same process, in a more highly controlled form, that results in the ossification of 'cartilage' bone.

Although the actual nature of bone does not differ whether it has developed directly in the dermis as dermal bone or as membrane bone or has replaced cartilage, nevertheless it is useful to distinguish the source of particular bony elements. Some are clearly surviving parts of the original dermal armour, others represent parts of the original cartilaginous endoskeleton. One of the important regions in which an internal support is required is the branchial or gill region. A comparatively simple basket affair, such as is found in the living lamprey and its ancestor the primitive anaspid *Jamoytius*, is all that is needed. In the heterostracans, however, there seems to have been a series of gill arches instead of this basket. These visceral arches are of some significance, since it was the anterior pair that became strongly developed and strengthened the margins of the mouth that became the jaws. The acquisition of jaws led to a major dietary break-through in the life of the vertebrates. A more active and aggressive life became possible, predation opened up a vast new potential for the vertebrates. However, it was not until bone had taken over from cartilage to form a strong internal supporting skeleton, that life outside of an aquatic medium became feasible.

Bone—a Structural Material

The success of the vertebrates and the considerable size attained by the terrestrial members of the group are, in large measure, due to the mechanical properties of the bone forming the endoskeleton. This tissue is, as has been mentioned, a two-phase material, comprising an organic matrix of fibrous collagen on which small crystallites of the mineral hydroxyapatite are packed. It is the combination of mechanical characteristics of the mineral and organic constituents that gives bone its unique structural properties. Apatite, alone, is much stronger in compression than in tension. All crystals have minute Griffith cracks causing localised concentration of stress; if tension is applied to the crystal it will ultimately fracture; if, however, it is subjected to repeated applications of a smaller tensile force, fracture will still ensue due to the gradual opening of the Griffith cracks. This latter is the well known condition of metal fatigue in aircraft. Compression on the other hand closes and minimises these cracks. The mineral element of bone can therefore, be expected to be stronger under compression than under tension.

Collagen, in contrast, is not rigid and deforms under compression; but when subjected to tension, the fibres stretch substantially before finally breaking. The combination of these two elements in bone produced a tissue with a high compressive and tensile strength. In discussions of its properties, bone is often compared to reinforced concrete, the organic matrix corresponding to the steel mesh and the apatite to the concrete poured round it. If this analogy were correct, bone would not have the high tensile strength it in fact possesses. A more apt analogy has recently been suggested by Currey[48,49] who has compared bone to a two-phase material such as fibre-glass. In this latter material there are glass fibres with a high modulus of elasticity embedded in an epoxy resin matrix with a low modulus of elasticity. The resulting material has a strength higher than either of the two components taken separately. As Currey states, 'the increased strength is attained because any cracks forming in the stiff fibres, which would normally spread right through the whole structure and cause it to fail, run into the flabby matrix, which will not transmit the crack, but will merely deform'. He further points out that bone is essentially comparable, since apatite does not occur in bulk with collagen fibres running through it, but, instead, in very small crystals which can be compared to the glass fibres of fibre-glass. The size of the apatite crystals is so small that there is little likelihood that they could contain any Griffith cracks; but, even if they did, with strong tensional forces they would simply run into the surrounding collagen which, like the epoxy resin of fibre-glass, would simply take up the strain by deforming and not by rupturing. In this way it is possible to see how apatite in bone can have, contrary to all expectations, great strength in tension. Bone can thus be compared directly to fibre-glass and can be considered as a mass of glassy 'fibres' of apatite embedded in a flabby matrix of the protein collagen.

The peculiar properties of bone may lead to the conclusion that its fundamental role must be supportive. However, this 'fibre-glass' type of organisation occurred in the skin of the earliest vertebrates, where it had no supporting role to play. The remarkable properties of this material are simply a consequence of the way apatite crystals are seeded onto the collagen molecule, presumably by hydrogen bonding. It is only with the development of an internal skeleton and the adoption of life on land that bone was fully utilised as a structural material.

The bones of the post-cranial skeleton subserve two functions: they provide areas of attachment for muscles and transmit the loads produced by them and by the body weight. The shape of any bone reflects this duality; in general it will be substantially thicker in those areas transmitting stress, but thinned elsewhere. An extreme example of this is seen in the vertebrae of the terrestrial dinosaurs. The lines of major stress are shown as thick rods of bone connected only by thin lamellae giving an excavated appearance. Exactly the same principles pertain when the finer structures of weight-bearing bones, such as those of the limbs of land animals, are examined. The most frequently quoted bone in this context is the human femur. When sectioned and examined by the naked eye it can be seen that the trabeculae line up along the main lines of force that are exerted on the bone. These have been known and variously interpreted since the early part of last century. Comparisons were made between the arrangement of the trabeculae and a lamp-bracket and also a crane. There is no doubt that the alignment of the trabeculae follows basic engineering principles; the only problem is to find an exact parallel. The forces acting on the femur are entirely compressive. The action of the femur at the acetabulum, when taking the full weight of the body, has been shown by Garden[66] to be more like that of a screw than, say, a crane. When the weight of the body is transferred to the femur it twists the bone into the socket. The entire system of the lines of force indicated by the arrangement of the trabeculae confirms this interpretation. The lines of stress are distributed to the outer part of the bone—the compact

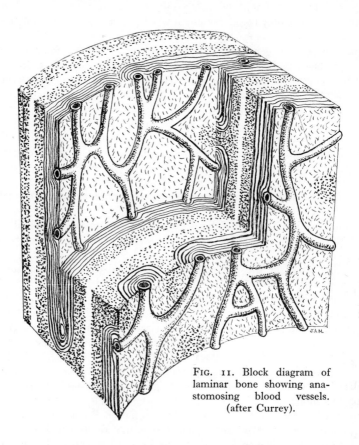

FIG. 11. Block diagram of laminar bone showing anastomosing blood vessels. (after Currey).

cortical bone, in constrast to the light open meshwork of the cancellous bone of the marrow. Essentially the weight-bearing bones of the limbs are hollow cylinders which are considerably stronger than, say, a solid rod of bone would be.

The load in the long bones, the body weight, is transmitted from the upper articular surface through the cortex, which is proportionately thickened in large terrestrial vertebrates such as the ruminants and the dinosaurs. Currey[47] has called the type of cortical bone characteristic of these animals 'laminar', to distinguish it from lamellar. The former consists, as the name implies, of a series of successive layers laid down by the retreating periosteum (Fig. 11). This type of bone contrasts with the more familiar Haversian, which essentially consists of a series of bony cylinders each with its central Haversian canal containing blood vessels. Currey[47] has shown that laminar bone is stronger than Haversian, and has further demonstrated that its vascular supply is more efficient. This being the case, the question arises as to why Haversian bone is the more common. Although laminar bone is more efficient, there is a delicate equilibrium between its structure and its vascular supply. Should the latter be disturbed in any way, the area of bone affected will die and be removed by osteoclasts. The tunnel so formed will become the site of an Haversian system which will automatically interfere with the delicate system of anastomosing blood vessels of the adjacent laminar bone, and so induce further production of Haversian systems, until the tissue is turned over from a laminar to an Haversian arrangement. Indeed, as Currey remarked, to regard the Haversian system as the unit of structure of compact bone is comparable to speaking of wrinkles as the basic units of skin!

The main advantage of Haversian bone is that it can be extensively remodelled and is thus particularly adaptable. This is especially important where an animal is subjected to differing physical stresses during its lifetime. From a static point of view, laminar bone is the more efficient but Haversian has the advantage of adaptability. In the final analysis a balance has to be struck between higher efficiency on the one hand and increased adaptability on the other; and it is the former that is generally sacrificed for the benefits that accrue from the latter.

Biomechanics of Joints

The general architecture of the bones is indicative of their function but it must be emphasised that this is primarily dependent on their relationship to one another. There are essentially three kinds of joints:

1. *Fibrous*. In these the bones are firmly united by collagenous fibres; for example in the sutures between the bones of the skull, in the interosseous ligaments that unite tibia and fibula, and in the alveoli of the jaws where the teeth are held in position by the Sharpey's fibres of the periodontal membrane passing from the alveolar bone of the socket into the cementum of the roots of the teeth.

2. *Cartilaginous*. In these the bones are united by fibrocartilage, which allows a small degree of movement such as between vertebral

centra with their intervertebral discs and in the symphysial joints, say
in the pubes.

3. *Synovial.* In these the joint is enclosed in a capsular ligament
containing synovial fluid which, since it is incompressible, renders
movement virtually frictionless.

Frost[65] has shown how the principles utilised in engineering, where
there are moving parts, apply in joints. The simplest case is found
where two surfaces move relative to one another and the bearing
surfaces are separated from one another by a thin layer of lubricant
which ideally adheres to them (Fig. 12a). This type of lubrication is
termed 'boundary layer lubrication' and occurs in slow moving joints.

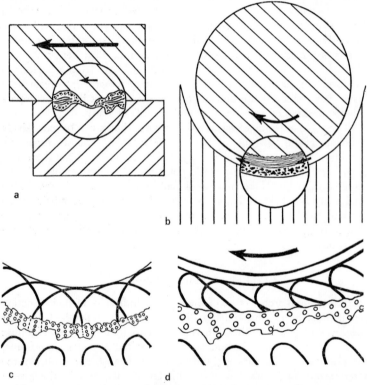

FIG. 12. a. Boundary layer lubrication, lubrication fills gaps between
bearing surfaces but is rubbed off where high spots touch; b. hydrodynamic lubrication, lubricant forced in between surfaces; c. diagram to
show relationship of hyaline cartilage, calcified cartilage and bone with
tangential alignment of collagen bundles; d. deformation due to shearing
force of joint motion. (after Frost).

There are small irregularities or high spots on the bearing surfaces which become abraided, where the thickness of the lubricant is insufficient to keep the two surfaces apart. Such abrasion of slow moving joints can be heard in the slight grating noise that occurs when one moves one's neck slowly.

With rapidly moving joints (i.e. synovial joints) the lubrication is hydrodynamic. In this case, the lubricant is forced between the two surfaces, and any heat that is generated is carried away by the lubricant (Fig. 12b). If the minimum thickness of the lubricant is greater than any irregularities in the bearing material, there will be no wear. At the same time, the thinner the layer of the lubricant, the faster the movement that is possible. When the lubricant fails to prevent contact between the two surfaces, large parts of the bearing surfaces are gouged out, a considerable amount of heat is generated, and wear is both severe and rapid. Such joints, which are termed osteoarthritic, may have shiny burnished bone surfaces where bone has been ground directly against bone. Normally there is bone growth around such joints, and this reactive proliferation may eventually result in the entire joint seizing up, so that further movement becomes impossible. While direct bone against bone articulation can be exceedingly painful, once the joint has solidified there is at least the consolation that there is, as well as no movement, no pain either.

The key factor with regard to the effective working of a synovial joint must be the nature of the bearing material, hyaline cartilage. An efficient bearing material must be smooth, and, although from the electron microscope it can be seen that jagged edges of collagen fibres project into the joint space, the lubricant is much thicker than the height of these protuberances. The lubricant must adhere to the bearing material and the mucin molecules of the synovial fluid in fact adhere to cartilage. Indeed, the cartilage soaks up the synovial fluid, which can be squeezed out whenever required. Finally a bearing material must have shear strength. Bundles of collagen that are strong and flexible but not elastic are embedded in a cement that is elastic but not strong. However, fibres from the underlying subchondral bone pass through the calcified cartilage to lie eventually in a tangential fashion at the surface (Fig. 12c). Deformation due to the shearing action involved in joint movement will be automatically corrected, once movement has stopped (Fig. 12d). One of the problems in hydrodynamic lubrication is to force the lubricant along the joint surface. This is accomplished by the presence of a cartilaginous meniscus or filler, the semilunar cartilages of the knee, which not only fill the gap in the joint when there is no movement involved but, once movement begins, force the synovial fluid between the joint surfaces.

The Static and Dynamic Skeleton

So far, the major components of the skeleton have been dealt with separately; but the skeleton as a whole also lends itself to analysis on simple engineering lines. It is easier to consider the skeleton from two different standpoints: firstly with regard to support, i.e. the static skeleton, in which numerous parallels can be seen between the vertebrate skeleton and problems of structural engineering; secondly with regard to movements, the dynamic skeleton, in which questions of orders of levers and mechanical advantage are relevant.

The basic tetrapod skeleton, as exemplified by the mammalian, can be considered as an axis supported on four columns, with a head and tail projecting beyond the supports. The most familiar parallel that is drawn is that between the skeleton and a bridge. Whereas all the elements in the bridge consist of steel, in the animal it is necessary to consider not only the bones, which, in the main, are compression struts, but also the associated muscles and ligaments, which, essentially, resist tensional forces. In a bridge the upper region is arched and is strengthened by numerous cross pieces; in the skeleton a comparable arrangement is effected by both neural spines and muscles. In the dog or cat the neural spines converge towards the middle of the back; in fact the backbone is under tension like a drawn bow. In contrast to this, there is the type of rigid backbone associated with, say, cows and horses, where a close structural similarity can be drawn between it and the Forth railway bridge. Here the arrangement of the neural spines is the same as that of the major steel girders around the main supports of the bridge. In both types of skeleton the head and tail are held by a cantilever arrangement whereby a single-arm girder is held by long braces. Similarly, the weight on the limbs will tend to splay them outwards (i.e. the forelegs forwards and the hindlegs backwards); this is counteracted by the front limbs bending backwards and the hind limbs forwards. The supports of the body, the limbs, are attached to the limb girdles, which in turn are connected to the backbone. The pelvic girdle is a rigid structure, fused to the vertebral column. The ball and socket joint on which the hind limbs rotate is perhaps one of the most firmly attached of all synovial joints. In the movement of the animal the main propulsive force comes from the hind limbs. In the pectoral girdle a different arrangement is to be found. The fore-limbs, together with the scapula, form the supporting pillar; but in this case the girdle is attached to the vertebral column, or more accurately onto the ribs, by a muscular sling. The sling musculature is so organised that the weight of the body pulls the scapulae against the rib-cage, thus tightening the effective holding power of the connection between the limbs and the axial skeleton. There is no bony union between the pectoral girdle and the verteral column because the anterior part of the visceral cavity must be capable of free movement; the ribs have to be able to move in and out during breathing. Furthermore, the anterior limbs take the main shock of landing, and a muscular sling is a more effective shock absorber. In the first vertebrates to venture on land these factors of supporting the body in air and off the ground did not apply. The fins of the advanced crossopterygian fish were simply struts which, although capable of being turned forwards to act as limbs, merely projected laterally from the ventro-lateral margins of the body, with the belly dragging along the ground. In the earliest amphibians the body was held off the ground, the humeri and femora projecting laterally from the sides of the body with the forearms and legs held vertically. The body was held by a sling-like action of the limbs and the animal was perfectly stable. Progression, however, was rather slow and ponderous. In the next major advance, found in the mammal-like reptiles and in the dinosaurs, the limbs were brought in under the body. This opened up greater potentialities for locomotion. The stride, and consequently the speed, were increased. The corollary of this, however, is that the animals were now much more unstable. Fortunately, this advance in the mode of locomotion went hand in hand with improved muscular co-ordination. Had it not been so, the dinosaurs and mammals would have spent most of their time just floundering about!

Once this type of posture had evolved, the specialisation of the limbs from the point of view of working levers can be examined. There are three orders of lever which all naturally occur (Fig. 13a–c).[236] First order levers are those whose fulcrum is situated between the weight and the effort. This is typified in the nodding motion of the head. In the second order lever the weight is positioned between the fulcrum and the effort, as, for example, when one stands on one's toes. With third order levers the effort is between the fulcrum and weight, as in lifting the forearm. It is in fact the third order lever system that is important in limb movements. The proportions of the different parts and functions of the limbs can be explained in terms of their differences of mechanical advantage. Where, for example, the main line of action of the limb muscles is close to the proximal articulation (i.e. the fulcrum), for any given contraction of muscle the range and speed of movement of the limb will be large, but comparatively weak (Fig. 13e). This type of limb characterises animals whose limbs have rapid movements. The mechanical advantage is said to be poor. The other extreme is where the muscle action is far removed from the fulcrum. For the same given muscular contraction, the range of movement will be less than in the previous example and so will the speed; but on the other hand there

E

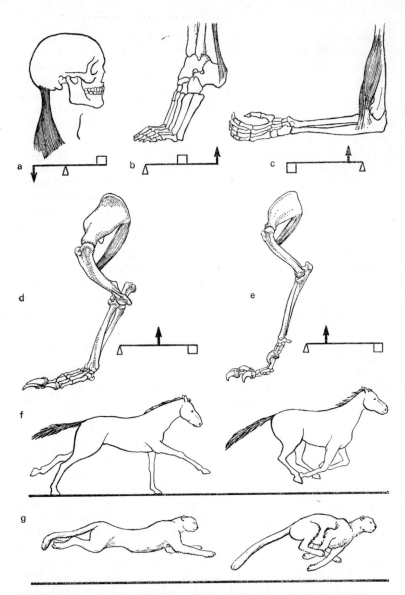

FIG. 13. a. First order lever; b. second order lever; c. third order lever; d. badger forelimb with good mechanical advantage; e. cheetah forelimb with poor mechanical advantage; f. horse showing stride with rigid backbone; g. cheetah showing stride with flexible backbone. (after Hildebrand).

will be greater power (Fig. 13d). The mechanical advantage in this instance is good.

Animals do not fall neatly into one or other of these categories. Digging animals, such as the armadillo and the badger, have limbs with good mechanical advantage, whereas animals specialised for speed, such as the horse, the deer and the cheetah, have limbs with poor mechanical advantage.[81,196] The majority of mammals fall somewhere between these two extremes, but in spite of this it is frequently possible to suggest from the proportions of the limbs, the locomotory habits of the animals concerned. To increase speed of movement it is important to increase the length of the stride. The only way of increasing the stride of, say, a horse, in which the vertebral column is rigid, is by swinging the scapula forwards with the fore limb. In contrast, in the dog, or more especially the cheetah, the spine itself is extremely flexible and is able to spring like a bow, so that the stride is vastly increased (Fig.13f, g). Indeed it has been suggested by some authors,[81] presumably in their lighter moments, that a cheetah with its legs amputated could by means of its vertebral column alone 'run' at about 6 m.p.h.

As previously mentioned, the increase in the powers of locomotion and the lessening of stability were coupled with concomitant improvements in muscular co-ordination, with which must be associated a greater awareness of the environment. This is particularly the case when it comes to the development of bipedalism, especially in man. As well as the greater muscular co-ordination required, the forelimbs are freed from ordinary locomotory functions and are able to take on the manipulative role normally assigned to the teeth, at least in the mammals. Bipedalism has occurred in many different groups such as the carnivorous dinosaurs, birds and kangaroos, where the problems of maintaining stability have been overcome in different ways. The most unstable condition is in man where the weight of the body has to be restricted over a narrow zone.

Although there has been a great deal of emphasis on the skeleton, it is important to remember that the form of the bones is a direct reflection of their function. Their shape depends simply on the muscles acting upon them. A study of the skeleton should resolve itself into a consideration of the behaviour of the animal concerned. In illustration of this point it is worth considering the bipedal goat described by Slijper.[191] This animal was born without any forelimbs and hence was quite incapable of walking about like any normal goat. In spite of its handicap it habitually walked on its hind limbs, just as a dog can do if trained. The significant feature about the bipedal goat is the form of its vertebral column, which is unlike that of any goat; the direction of the neural spines is quite different and the column as a whole has a sinuous curvature not unlike that of the human skeleton. It seems evident that the skeleton does not determine the activity of the animal, but rather the functioning of the animal determines its form. The evolutionary changes in the skeletons of the vertebrates that can be traced through geological time simply give an account of changing patterns of behaviour.

5 : Brains

The evolution of the vertebrate skeleton cannot be divorced from that of the central nervous system; with increased powers of locomotion there follows improved muscular coordination and, its corollary, a greater awareness of the environment. This can be clearly seen in the evolution of the gross morphology of the brain. Although the internal architecture of fossil brains cannot be ascertained, it is possible to draw a number of conclusions from the relative proportions of their different parts. Such studies are actually based on the examination of endocranial casts; in only a few instances, as in the cephalaspids, can the details be made out with as much precision as in living animals.[197] Nevertheless a number of useful observations have been made which, when combined with the examination of the brains of living vertebrates and a study of their embryological development, can give a reasonably comprehensive picture of the evolution of the central nervous system.

Agnathan Brains

It is reasonable to assume that the basic pattern of the vertebrate central nervous system was established in the early jawless forms, and perhaps, to be exemplified in their living descendants, the lampreys and hagfish. In the larval lamprey or ammocoete the hollow nerve cord is swollen anteriorly into three parts which foreshadow the future fore-, mid- and hind-brain. Fundamentally the fore-brain is concerned with the sense of smell, the mid-brain with sight and the hind-brain with hearing and balance. The fore-brain is divided into anteriorly the telencephalon or cerebrum which, in the agnathans, consists of only the olfactory lobes, and posteriorly the diencephalon, including the pineal organ dorsally and the hypophysis ventrally. The mid-brain, or mesencephalon, with its optic lobes receives sensory stimuli from all somatic sources, associates and synthesises and originates the motor responses to them. The hind-brain consists of two parts. The anterior part, the metencephalon or cerebellum, is, in the ammocoete and lamprey, simply a transverse commissure in front of the fourth ventricle. The cerebellum is concerned with muscular coordination and balance. The posterior part of the hind-brain, the myelencephalon or medulla oblongata, is primarily responsible for the regulation of all visceral activity, such as respiration.

The arrangement of the different parts of the brain in the ammocoete is somewhat altered in the adult lamprey as a consequence of the development of the sucker. This causes a dorsal flexure of the brain so that the diencephalon is pushed up and over the telencephalon (Fig. 14a, b). This flexure results in the displacement of the nasohypophyseal opening from the ventral surface to the dorsal.

In the cephalaspids the nasohypophyseal opening is also dorsal, but this can be attributed to specialisation for a benthonic life. Neither explanation appears to hold for the dorsal position of the opening in the anaspids, which had neither a sucker nor a benthonic habit. Perhaps, after all, the dorsal position of the olfactory apparatus was a primitive one and is merely exaggerated in the lamprey. However, both cephalaspids and lampreys are unusual in having paired olfactory lobes but a single nasal organ. The brain of the cephalaspids is well known as a result of the classic researches of Stensiö[197] and appears to be similar to that of the lamprey, although the dorsal flexure is not so marked.[62] The major difference between them is the presence of two prominent dorsal lobes on the hind-brain of the cephalaspids (Fig. 14c, d), which were clearly related to the lateral and dorsal sensory fields. These organs, extensions of the labyrinth of the ear, responded to sound and vibration and were a specialisation of the acoustico-lateralis system. The organisation of the brain in the lamprey and cephalaspids conforms to the basic vertebrate pattern, with only minor modifications.

In contrast, the central nervous system of the hagfish, the other group of living agnathans, is very different from those of the lampreys and cephalaspids.[25,62] The hagfish brain is very flat, due to its embryological development between a tough membrane and a dense yolk. There is a well developed telencephalon with paired olfactory lobes, although, as in the lampreys and cephalaspids, there is only a single nasal sac; a paired diencephalon but no pineal organ; a reduced mesencephalon and a medulla oblongata. There is no cerebellum (Fig. 14e). The reduction of the mid-brain is associated with the atrophy of the eyes. This loss of the visual sense is compensated by the enhancement of the sense of smell, which is especially important for a burrower and scavenger. Apart from their more obvious specialisations the hagfish appear to represent a more primitive grade of organisation than, say, the lampreys.

Stensiö[197,199,204] has long claimed that the two groups of living Agnatha are in no way related to one another and that the cyclostomes are of diphyletic origin, a view to which little exception can be taken. Furthermore, he has contended that the hagfish are probably descended

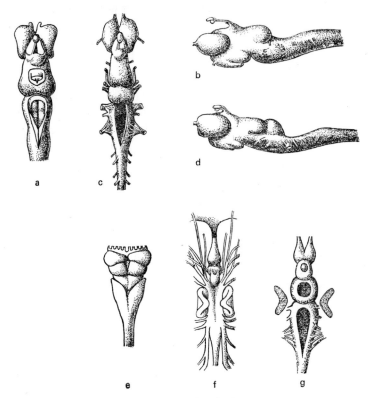

FIG. 14. Agnathan brains

a, b. lamprey, dorsal and lateral views; c. d. cephalaspid, dorsal and lateral views; e. hagfish, dorsal view; f. heterostracan, dorsal view (interpretation of Stensiö); g. heterostracan, dorsal view (interpretation of Whiting and Halstead Tarlo). (after Stensiö, Bone, Whiting and Halstead Tarlo).

from the heterostracans, and with this in mind has reconstructed the brain of the latter (Fig. 14f). Stensiö's[203] account of the heterostracan brain would seem to have little to do with that of the hagfish. He portrays the diencephalon as partially overlying the telencephalon as in the hagfish embryo where there is such a downward flexure. However, this flexure in the hagfish is transitory and is due to the head temporarily sinking into the yolk. Behind the diencephalon with its prominent pineal, which is not known in the hagfish, is a sausage-shaped object, the mid-brain according to Stensiö,[199] who identifies it in some of his diagrams as the cerebellum. A large medulla oblongata extends anteriorly well beyond the semi-circular canals of the ear, with a well defined commissure at its anterior margin. This brain as reconstructed by Stensiö is rather peculiar and, although somewhat reminiscent of the lamprey brain, is in no sense comparable with that of the hagfish.

Whiting and I[249] have examined the somewhat limited fossil material on which Stensiö's conclusions were based, and it is apparent that there is little support for his claims. The under surfaces of the dorsal plates of the heterostracan dermal armour have impressions showing the position of the related soft tissues. The outline of these markings conforms closely to the upper surface of the brain, the most prominent being a deep pit in the midline, which is generally agreed to have housed the pineal organ, and a pair of arcuate grooves pointing towards the midline, grooves which must have been made by the two vertically orientated semi-circular canals of the ear. The midline impressions in front of and behind these canals, which must have corresponded to the positions of the mid- and hind-brains, are rather faintly marked. Overall, the morphology of the dorsal surface of the heterostracan brain is clearly shown on the internal surface of the dermal armour. In view of this it is surprising to find Stensiö interpolating a layer of cartilage between the central nervous system and the dermal armour (especially when his restoration of the brain is so very detailed), to act as a roof for the brain. In fact it is much more likely that only a single meninge separated the two and so allowed the plates to be effectively moulded by the configuration of the upper surface of the C.N.S. (Fig. 14g).

There is no sign of the development of optic lobes, but this may be due to the fact that the eyes were not very advanced. There is clear evidence that two pairs of preotic somites, which in all known vertebrates, including the lamprey, give rise to the extrinsic muscles of the eyes, had not yet migrated to the orbits.[227] The position of the first preotic somite, the premandibular, is unknown and cannot be inferred from the fossils; so we cannot be sure that the heterostracans were unable to move their eyes (Fig. 16d).

In front of the pineal organ one can occasionally, as in the hagfish, see a faint median groove, which Stensiö[203] interprets as the single nasal sac. Since in many specimens there are impressions of paired nasal capsules at the anterior margin of the carapace, Stensiö's interpretation is redundant. The most reasonable interpretation of this impression is that it was made by the telencephalon. This gives an alternative restoration of the heterostracan brain: it was in no way flexed either dorsally or ventrally, as might be expected in the most primitive of the vertebrates; in fact, it was little more than a simple nerve cord swollen in particular regions. The hind-brain consisted of a typical medulla with its fourth ventricle, its anterior margin representing a simple primitive cerebellum. The mid-brain was similarly extremely primitive in that the iter was wide open and the optic lobes not developed. The two parts of the fore-brain were clearly in tandem; although there is no evidence of the exact outline of the olfactory lobes, it would seem a fairly safe assumption, in view of the paired nasal organs, that they too must have been similarly paired.

The heterostracan brain was, therefore, clearly the simplest and most primitive of any recorded vertebrate. It was less specialised than those of the lampreys or cephalaspids, although both could easily be derived from it. The development of a single nasal organ would seem to take the lampreys, cephalaspids and hagfish off the main line of vertebrate evolution. The structure of the heterostracan brain, however, is such that it provides the ideal starting point for the subsequent developments of the C.N.S. seen in the higher vertebrates.

Gnathostome Brains

Although examination of the brains of living vertebrates can show developmental trends within the various classes, it is not always possible to suggest how one could have evolved from another, simply because, with few exceptions, the living vertebrates are the end-products of long evolutionary histories. This is particularly so with modern bony fish, the teleosts. Their brains can easily be derived ultimately from that of a larval lamprey or heterostracan, but they show no obvious pattern of subsequent evolution within the group. In the bony fish the fore-, mid- and hind-brains are unevenly developed, exaggeration of any of these parts depending on the prominence of the sense organs with which they are associated. (In those fish in which sight is the predominant sense the mid-brain is much enlarged; where smell is the most important, the fore-brain is elaborated. The hind-brain may develop extra lobes in conjunction with electric organs). All the many examples that can be cited serve to emphasise the adaptive evolution of the bony fish and show that this group, at least, is likely to be of little value in tracing the main trends of the evolution of the central nervous system in the terrestrial vertebrates.

It is frequently believed that the cartilaginous fish are more primitive than the teleosts, but here too this group shows a considerable degree of specialisation. The sharks and their relatives have evolved an exceedingly acute sense of smell, their brains have well developed cerebral hemispheres as well as a large cerebellum, indicating a high degree of muscular coordination and control over position. Such specialisations had not evolved in the brains of the early jawed vertebrates. Amongst living vertebrates, it is the Amphibia that appear to have the most primitive type of brain (Fig. 15a).

The major changes that can be traced in the evolution of the brain of the higher vertebrates can be correlated with the change from an aquatic to a terrestrial life, with the increasing dominance of the sense of smell. This change is best illustrated by examining the proportions of the different bones making up the skull roof in crossopterygian fish, amphibians, reptiles and mammals. This sequence shows a gradual lengthening of the snout and a compensatory shortening of the posterior table of the skull. As the move onto land involves life in 'two dimensions' instead of three, it is not surprising to find the acoustico-lateralis system becoming superfluous and ultimately lost, leaving only a variably developed sense of hearing. On the other hand the olfactory organs require a much higher degree of sensitivity, hence the improvement of the olfactory apparatus and the enlargement of the snout and braincase (Fig. 22).

To outline the changes that took place in the transition from water to land, it is best to consider the situation in the major groups and then trace separately the differing fates of the main parts of the brain. In the most primitive type of brain the olfactory lobes of the fore-brain are concerned with smell, the mid-brain, with its optic lobes, with sight, and the cerebellum with sensory structures in the body muscles and with balance and the acoustico-lateralis system. In fishes and amphibians the mid-brain, although primarily concerned with vision, receives in its dorsal part pathways from other sensory centres such as the ear, lateral-line and nasal organs.

In fact, sensory stimuli from all somatic sources are associated, synthesised, and the motor responses originated, from the mid-brain. In the reptiles the roof of the mid-brain, the tectum, is still a major association centre, but the cerebral hemispheres become equally important as correlation centres (Fig. 15b). This was probably due to the sense of smell, the more posteriorly situated association centres shifting forwards for closer contact with the olfactory centres. At the same time, with improved methods of locomotion and the greater degree of instability of the animals, the cerebellum became further developed. This part of the reptilian brain is concerned with the coordination of motor activities and the maintenance of posture. Birds show the logical extension of this trend, as do the pterosaurs (Fig. 15c). The mid-brain

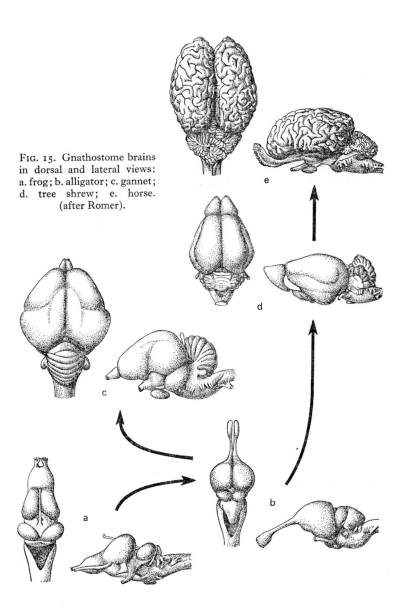

FIG. 15. Gnathostome brains in dorsal and lateral views: a. frog; b. alligator; c. gannet; d. tree shrew; e. horse. (after Romer).

still retains its basic optic function, but the brain is now dominated by the cerebral hemispheres and the cerebellum. The former are concerned with the complex instinctive behavioural patterns of birds, the latter with balance and muscular coordination.

There is a somewhat comparable development in the mammals (Fig. 15d, e). The cerebral hemispheres and cerebellum are so expanded that they overlap both the mid-brain and diencephalon. Almost all the functions primitively assigned to the mid-brain become transferred or subordinate to the cerebral hemispheres; even visual sensations are integrated here, with the exception of the eye reflexes. The mid-brain now links the fore- and hind-brains but retains some regulating activities. The cerebrum, having gradually become more and more important as the major association centre of the mammalian brain, becomes the seat of intelligence and the ability to learn.

A number of evolutionary trends can be followed in the history of the cerebral hemispheres, although in only a few cases does any evidence come from fossils. The striking cerebral enlargement seen in the primates, which has reached its apogee in ourselves, would seem to be due in large measure to the reduction in the sense of smell and an improvement in the senses of sight and balance. Essentially, the association of what the eye sees with the delicate control of the limbs, especially the manipulative actions of the forelimbs, led to the human condition. The increased muscular coordination required for life in the trees and equally as a biped, and the greater awareness in a three-dimensional environment all resulted in bigger and, more importantly, better brains. The paradox of this situation is that it was the reduction of the importance of these same sense organs and the increase in the sense of smell that made possible the very advances that mark the success of the mammals. Yet, for still further advance, the process has had apparently to go into reverse. In fact this is not quite so, the gains resulting from the emphasis on smell were not lost, but rather a bonus was added in the further development of sight and improved muscular coordination.

6 : Primitive Jawed Vertebrates

Head Segmentation

It has long been recognised from the embryological development of the vertebrates that the major structures in the head region are serially repeated. This is well illustrated by Goodrich's[2] classic diagram of the head of the embryo dogfish (Fig. 16a). It is important to recognise that in this metameric segmentation the jaws are modified gill arches. In all living vertebrates the hyoidean is the most anterior gill slit; this is not normally present in the adult except in some fish where it forms the spiracle. The hyoidean, or third segment, arch lies behind its gill slit, the mandibular or second arch in front. In his classic work on the cephalaspids, Stensiö[197] showed that the course of the cranial nerves could be traced. From his identification of the cranial nerves he concluded that the cephalaspids must have possessed a prespiracular gill pouch. Romer[12] and Watson[240] have suggested that Stensiö's work indicates the existence of two pouches in front of the hyoidean. If either of these interpretations were proved correct, it would mean that the cephalaspids were much more primitive than any other group of agnathan, representing a stage not found during the embryological development of the most primitive of living vertebrates. Despite the unlikelihood of this happening, this interpretation of the cephalaspids has been accepted with great enthusiasm. With the recognition that the vertebrate head exhibited a fundamental segmentation, it was firmly believed that somewhere in the history of the vertebrates there must have been an animal that possessed the full complement of structures in the two anterior segments, the premandibular and mandibular. Such an animal would be expected to have had both premandibular and mandibular gill slits with the appropriate gill bars behind them. The situation described in the cephalaspids fitted this view perfectly. However, Lindström[122] pointed out that, although all the structures described by Stensiö actually existed, he had misnumbered the cranial nerves. In fact the situation in the cephalaspids was the same as that

65

known in the lampreys. This meant that the identification of the gill
pouches was also in error and that there was no basis for claiming that
these animals had any pouches in front of the hyoidean; so the
cephalaspids were once more brought into line with all other vertebrates.

However, the arrangement of the gill lamellae in the cephalaspids
and lampreys is fundamentally different from that in the jawed vertebrates, since they are situated medial to the visceral arches and in the

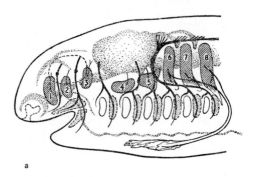

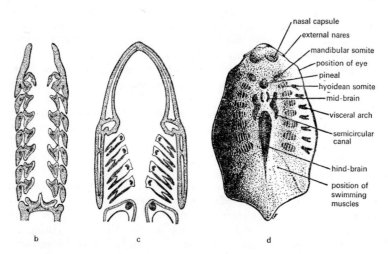

Fig. 16. a. Diagram of early stage in elasmobranch ontogeny: somites
hashured, cartilage stippled, cranial nerves dorsal roots heavy lines,
ventral roots fine lines; b, c. longitudinal, horizontal sections to show
relationship of gill structures to skeleton, b. lamprey, c. fish; d. internal
surface of dorsal plate of cyathaspid heterostracan with impressions made
by underlying soft parts. (after Goodrich, Jarvik, Halstead Tarlo and
Whiting).

adults form sac-like structures, whereas in the later vertebrates the gills lie lateral to the visceral arches (Fig. 16b, c). As Jarvik[95] has correctly emphasised, it is quite impossible to derive one condition from the other. It is generally believed that the agnathan heterostracans had the same type of gill structure as the lampreys and cephalaspids. Oval impressions on the inner surface of the main plates of the armour are invariably stated to have been made by the gill pouches; furthermore the longitudinal grooves and ridges on these impressions are identified by Stensiö[199,204] and Jarvik[6] as marking the position of the gill lamellae. However, Whiting and I[227] have demonstrated that these impressions are of somites, and that the longitudinal grooves simply represent their longitudinally orientated muscle plates, as in all vertebrates (Fig. 16d). Any other explanation, with visceral structures impinging on the dorsal surface of the animal, would make the heterostracans some of the most highly evolved and aberrant vertebrates—which seems most unlikely. The recognition of the impressions made by somites brings the heterostracans into line with the rest of the vertebrates and is consistent with comparative anatomy and embryology. Any interpretation which does not so conform should always be treated with caution.

It is known that the lampreys and anaspids have branchial supports in the form of complicated baskets, which are hardly comparable to the branchial arches of the jawed vertebrates. On the other hand, in the heterostracans there are Y-shaped impressions made by the visceral arches, and these seem to suggest the positioning of anterior and posterior hemibranchs of the gills exactly as in the gnathostomes. In this respect, as in others, the heterostracans appear to represent the basic condition from which the higher vertebrates evolved; they were the 'pre-gnathostomes'. The mandibular arch however had no associated gill slit, but acted to support the mouth. Any increase in this role and consequent enlargement of the elements concerned would produce de facto a jaw. The complex process of telescoping the premandibular arch and the elimination of the two anterior gill slits is so obviated. In any event, it should be remembered that there is no reason whatsoever for believing in the existence of a primitive vertebrate with a fully segmented head; the mere fact that this is the part of the animal that faces the world and takes in the food must ensure the alteration of such hypothetical perfection.

Acanthodian Fish and Jaws

The next stage in the evolution of the jaws is found in the acanthodian fishes which first appeared in rocks of Silurian age, some

440 million years ago. Their anatomy was described by Watson[239] in a classic paper in which he showed that the jaws were formed of separate elements in exactly the same way as typical branchial arches. With the development of jaws articulating with the cranium, this latter had of necessity to be rigid. Watson claimed that the hyoid arch, in contrast to that of primitive fish, took no part in the suspension of jaws

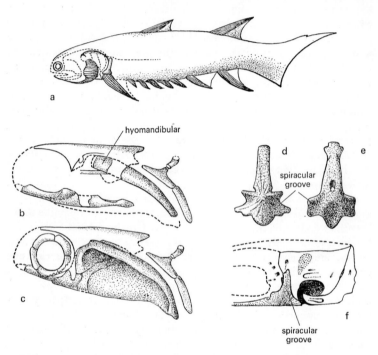

FIG. 17. a. Acanthodian fish, *Euthacanthus*; b. *Acanthodes*, ossified cranium with hyomandibular and dorsal part of first branchial arch; c. as b., but with palatoquadrate and circumorbital bones added; d, f. parasphenoid of primitive actinopterygian in ventral and lateral views; e. *Acanthodes*, anterior basal element in ventral view. (after Miles).

onto the cranium, and that it was essentially an unmodified branchial arch. From the presence of gill rakers he concluded that in the acanthodians the hyoidean gill slit was still fully functional. In view of this, he introduced the term Aphetohyoidea, meaning 'free hyoid', for a grade of vertebrates intermediate between the agnathans and true fishes. This concept was accepted with alacrity. It was believed that in the evolution of the jaws there must have been a stage when they were formed from the mandibular arch alone and the succeeding hyoidean was unaltered. From Watson's[239] account the hyoidean slit appears to be greatly constricted by the enormous increase in size of the mandibular arch, so that it is difficult to see how it could have functioned adequately. Furthermore, Stensiö[198] pointed out that the lateral line system crossed over what Watson claimed was an open gill slit and, at the same time, it was noted that the presence of gill rakers did not necessarily mean the existence of a functional gill. Recently Miles[124,125] has conclusively demonstrated that the dorsal part of the hyoid arch, the hyomandibular, articulates with the otic capsule, and in consequence must be concerned with the jaw suspension (Fig. 17b, c). The entire basis for the existence of the aphetohyoideans has now been removed. Miles has also provided evidence of the existence of a spiracle in the acanthodians, showing that the hyoidean gill had already been reduced. The ventral part of the slit has been shown by Jarvik[93] to have survived throughout the vertebrates up to and including man, where it is represented by the groove or pocket housing the salivary glands.

The suspension of the jaws from the cranium through both the upper jaw and the hyomandibular, which occurs in the acanthodians and in primitive cartilaginous fish, is termed *amphistyly*. In more advanced cartilaginous fish and in the bony fish, the jaws are suspended by the hyomandibular alone, allowing a much greater gape, an obvious advantage since it means that larger prey can be tackled. In the amphibians and higher vertebrates, the upper jaw once again becomes directly attached to the cranium, the hyomandibular now forming the stapes, the main sound-conducting ear ossicle.

The jaw articulation of the acanthodians would appear to have been more advanced than Watson[239] claimed. But it seems reasonable to accept the acanthodian condition as primitive, since the increase in the dimensions of the mandibular arch must, of necessity, have impinged on the adjacent hyoidean. Even if the hyomandibular did not articulate directly with the jaws, the disposition of this arch must have been such that it was bound to have assisted in the bracing and support of the jaw mechanism as a whole.

Until recently, there has also been much controversy on the relationship of the acanthodians to the other fishes. Watson[239] believed that they were not related to any group of living fish. Stensiö,[198] Holmgren[83] and latterly Jarvik[6,95] have linked them with the cartilaginous fish, but recently Miles[124,125] has shown that their true affinities are with the bony fish. This is based in part on the virtual identity of the parasphenoid bone of the bony fish with the anterior basal element of the acanthodians (Fig. 17d–f), the method of articulation of the

F

hyomandibular, and the presence of large hyoidean gill covers. The detailed similarity between the structure of the tail of the primitive bony fish *Cheirolepis* and that of the acanthodians is not considered to be of much significance by Miles[124,125] but it is nonetheless striking for all that and does, in any event, support his main thesis.

Arthrodires (Placoderms) and Cartilaginous Fish

Since the acanthodians do not seem to be related to the cartilaginous fish, the question of where these latter came from naturally arises. Contemporary with the acanthodians was a large and varied group of armoured jawed fishes characterised by a prominent neck joint in their armour. These were the arthrodires, which seem to have been successful carnivores of the Devonian period. The most primitive of this Class possessed an armour of small polygonal plates or tesserae, but in the later forms a well-defined system of large plates evolved (Fig. 18a–c). Several groups looked remarkably like modern skates and rays and, although they were not directly related to them, they have tended to support the contention of Stensiö[6,95,200] and his school that the arthrodires are elasmobranchiomorphs. The detailed anatomical similarities that have been demonstrated by Stensiö cannot all be attributed to convergent evolution. Nevertheless this view is still contested in certain quarters. In recent years, however, Ørvig[150,151] has described a remarkable arthrodire from the Devonian of Germany which would seem definitely to establish the relationships of the cartilaginous fish and arthrodires (although even here his conclusions have been disputed by Patterson[156]). This animal, *Ctenurella*, belongs to the ptyctodont group of arthrodires, the pattern of skull roofing bones establishing beyond any doubt that this genus was a true arthrodire (Fig. 18d, e). The quite sensational aspect of this fossil is its general resemblance to the living chimaeras or rabbit-fish. These weird looking cartilaginous fish possess a number of odd specialisations which had been thought unique. However, these same features, such as the paired rostral cartilages, the peculiar form of the copulatory organs and the dorsal fins, occurred in *Ctenurella* also. The conclusion that the chimaeras are surviving arthrodires is inescapable (see also Miles[126]).

Clearly the major division between the cartilaginous and the bony fish existed at the very beginning of the fossil record of the jawed vertebrates. Unfortunately, there is no evidence which links them to the heterostracans, although it can be safely assumed that they must have originated from animals at that structural level.

Both the arthrodires and acanthodians had efficient jaws; White has shown that the neck joint in the former allowed the skull to be raised,

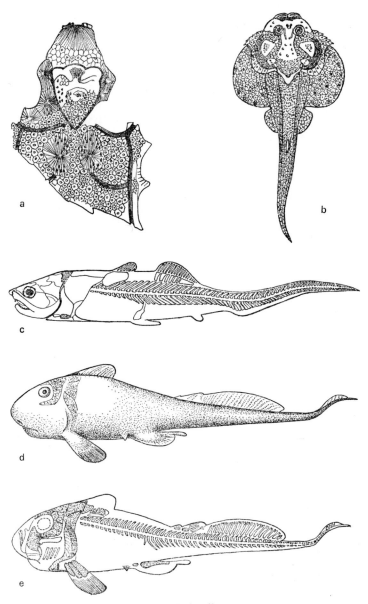

FIG. 18. Arthrodires

a. *Radotina*, primitive tessellated arthrodire, dorsal view of skull (Lower Devonian); b. *Gemuendina*, dorsal view (Lower Devonian); c. *Coccosteus*, lateral view (Middle Devonian); d, e. *Ctenurella*, restoration and skeleton in lateral view (Middle Devonian). (after Gross, Stensiö and Ørvig).

thus giving considerable increase in gape. Larger and more effective bites of the prey could then be taken! To have efficient means of dealing with one's food is not enough; it is equally necessary for it to be caught, which in turn demands precise control of swimming movements. The development of paired fins accomplished this, but by different means in the arthrodires and acanthodians. In both groups, as with the ostracoderms, the fins initially acted as stabilisers whose main function was to prevent undue roll. In the acanthodians there were pectoral and pelvic fins, and, in some forms, an additional series of smaller accessory fins between the main paired fins (Fig. 17a). In all cases the fins were triangular with broad bases, and were probably not capable of much independent movement. A strong spine supported the leading edge of each fin. The arrangement of the fins in the acanthodians is generally accepted as evidence of the origin of paired fins from a lateral fin-fold.[244] There is no doubt that stabilising projections can be developed from this region of the body in a variety of ways.

In the primitive arthrodires such stabilisers were merely lateral spines developed by the lateral growth of the ventro-lateral margin of the shoulder armour. Subsequently they became movable and received both endoskeletal and muscular supports. The bony exoskeletal spine was reduced until it was confined to a short projection protecting the leading edge of the fin. There was a concentration of radial elements at the base of the fin, so that the part nearest the body was much narrower than that farther away. For some reason Stensiö[200] and Jarvik[6] believe that this type of fin, which characterises the latest arthrodires, was the most primitive. They believe that fins developed from the muscularisation of the ventro-lateral crest of the body wall. This has clearly occurred in these latest arthrodires, but it seems anomalous to suggest then that the earliest arthrodire with their massive lateral spines should be the most advanced. If Stensiö's and Jarvik's theory is stood on its head, a much more reasonable account emerges.

On the subject of arthrodire fins, mention should be made of the most bizarre, the antiarch. This group of arthrodires became microphagous, probably occupying the ecological niche formerly filled by the ostracoderms. Although they had jaws, these were very weak; in addition, the dorsal position of their eyes further indicates a benthonic mode of life (Fig. 19a, c). In spite of their seemingly passive nature and their extreme vulnerability with a vast array of carnivorous near, and more remote, relatives, they were incredibly successful for a period of some 20 million years. Antiarchs are found in freshwater deposits in the Arctic, the Antarctic and virtually every continent in between. When these fossils were first discovered by Hugh Miller, he thought they were a cross between a fish and an arthropod. This impression is not as silly

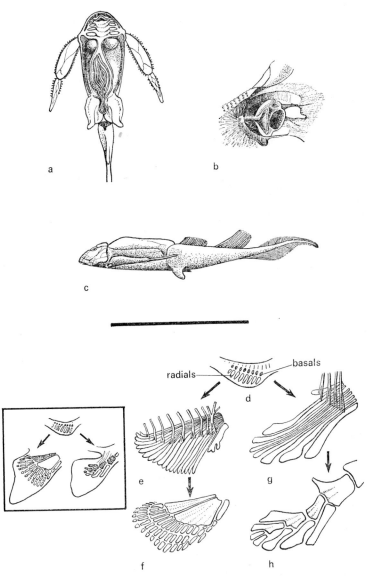

radials

basals

d

e

f

g

h

FIG. 19. a–c. Antiarch: a. Restoration of soft parts in ventral view showing accessory breathing organ and spiral valve of gut; b. helmet process on which pectoral fin articulated; c. restoration in lateral view; d–h. evolution of paired fins: d. primitive condition to show basals (stippled) and radials; e, f. development of shark fin; g, h. development of rhipidistian fin; *Inset*: evolution of fins according to previous theory. (after Denison, Gross, Stensiö and Jarvik).

as it sounds, because the forelimbs of these fish were solidly encased in bone. The nerves and blood vessels and, of course, the muscles were inside the bony shell; indeed in the form of their limbs they paralleled the arthropods to an astonishing degree. The shoulder joint comprised perhaps the most unusual ball-and-socket joint throughout the vertebrates; there is a goblet-shaped extension from the wall of the socket and the limb is fitted round it (Fig. 19b). Watson[242] has shown that it was capable of moving only in the horizontal plane, and that it could be brought forward to project at right angles to the body and be tucked into the side. Some rotation was possible but in no circumstances could the antiarch 'walk' on the river bed with its 'legs', as portrayed by some authors. There was a further joint halfway down the limb, but exactly how this functioned is not really known.

Evolution of Paired Fins

The subsequent evolution of paired fins in both the cartilaginous and the bony fish reveals a striking example of parallel evolution. Initially both had a broad based triangular fin, composed of basal elements in the body wall and radials with associated muscles from the dorsal and ventral surfaces. This type of fin is well seen in the primitive shark *Cladoselache*, where it must have acted simply as a stabiliser and clearly was not capable of more sophisticated movement. In the next stage, the posterior margin of the fin was freed from the body wall, the base of the fin narrowed and in consequence greater freedom of movement became possible. This allowed the animal to exercise greater control over its movements. Until recently it was believed that the basal elements were freed from the body wall and became fused to form the three large cartilages, the pro-, meso- and meta-pterygia of the modern sharks, with the radials radiating from them. The base of the fin was thus greatly concentrated with the more distal elements fanning out, producing the highly manoeuvrable fin of the modern sharks. As well as this type of 'rayed' fin, there evolved a further type, having an axial skeleton. It was believed that in the latter the row of basals, once freed from the body wall, did not fuse but remained separate. However, at the same time, new radials were developed along the posterior edge of the row of basals. This type of 'lobe-fin' was equally narrowly based and also capable of a wide variety of movements. In fact it represents an equally viable improvement on the primitive broad based fin. It appears that there were two ways of evolving an efficient type of fin and that both were followed in the sharks.

The role of the basals in the development of these two types of fin has been re-examined recently by Jarvik[96] who has demonstrated that, although the basal parts of the shark fin were produced by fusion, this was the fusion of the radials and not the basals (Fig. 19e, f). In consequence, the interpretation of the lobe-finned sharks no longer involves the complete freeing of a row of basals or the development anew of an extra set of radials. All that is required is the development of one of the central rows of radials at the expense of those both in front and behind.

In essence, the same two basic ways of improving the potentialities of the paired fins can be traced in the bony fish. Here again, both lobed and rayed fins were developed, and in this case the differences are used to divide the bony fish into two major groups. In the ray-finned or actinopterygian fish, the primitive members possessed a single large fused basal metapterygium but this seems to be hardly distinguishable from the adjacent radials. In the later development of the fin there is no sign of the basals and the radials are much reduced; in fact they articulate directly with the shoulder girdle. The main web of the fin is supported by true fin-rays or lepidotrichia. Whereas in the primitive actinopterygians the fins were very fleshy, in the later forms the musculature was withdrawn into the body wall. The other line of fin improvement involved a concentration of the proximal elements with the exaggeration of the central radials. Once again the main body axis has been claimed to have developed from the freed basals forming the 'meta-pterygial stem'. But here too, Jarvik[96] has shown that, although fusion of the more proximal elements must have occurred, it was essentially of the radials (Fig. 19g, h). The main difference between the lobe-fin and ray-fin is that in the former the fin remains muscular and the skeletal elements always give a firm axial support to the fin.

Although the lobe-fins of the bony fish were of prime importance in the transition from water to land, their development was in no way connected with this future event. As with the sharks, it just so happened that this was one of the alternative ways of improving the efficiency of paired fins. It was simply a means of increasing the animal's control over its movements, and certainly was not in anticipation of leaving the water several tens of millions of years later. Changes that took place were concerned with immediate advantages to the life of the animal in the 'here and now' with not a thought of future generations. When we observe the modifications that occurred, we have the advantage of hindsight in knowing that the development of the bony lobe-fin led to the origin of the pentadactyl limb. But just because this is so, it does not mean that the development originated for this purpose. When studying major structural advances in the history of the vertebrates, it is necessary to forget as far as possible what they eventually led to, and to try and analyse them in the context of their own times, to see what they meant in the life of the animal concerned in the the environment it inhabited, and not in the light of the 'breakthrough' we now recognise it to have been.

7 : First Land Vertebrates

At first sight, one of the most dramatic events in the history of the vertebrates was the transition from an aquatic to a terrestrial environment. This entailed the change from gill to lung breathing and also involved fundamental changes in the skeleton. In water, the animal is supported by the medium in which it lives; out of water the streamlined shape is of little avail in locomotion. In air the body has to support its own weight on its limbs and the vertebral column has to be modified to prevent undue sagging. Similarly the sense organs meet different problems in the air. The lateral line system is of no use at all on land, whilst the olfactory organs must have their sensitivity greatly increased in order to be able to recognise the much more dilute nature of smells in air.

The Transition from Water to Land

However, it is important to realise that in the gradual transition from one medium to another the animal must always remain an efficient working whole. For an amphibian's ancestor to replace its mode of respiration by lungs, there must have been a stage where both gills and lungs functioned side by side. Similarly, though modified fins and vertebral column allowed the animal to travel on land, nevertheless the capacity to swim and feed in water had to be retained for successful competition with ordinary fish.

Why should these major structural changes have come about? The first amphibians are known from rocks of Devonian age, a time when there was very little life on land, apart from plants and insects. There was clearly little alimentary incentive for carnivorous animals to venture onto land. Therefore the development of the structures which characterise the Amphibia must clearly be related to something other than a hypothetical desire to conquer the land! In fact all the changes were simply developments enabling the animals concerned to continue life as successful fish.[238]

The explanation is to be found in the conditions in which the majority of fishes lived during the Devonian. With the exception of the sharks, they inhabited freshwater rivers and lakes. This was at a time when according to the geological evidence, there were periodic and probably seasonal droughts and floods. During the dry seasons the water would tend to become fouled, the supply of dissolved oxygen would be used up and the fishes would die. However, there was no shortage of atmospheric oxygen, because of the extensive plant cover. Any fish that could avail itself of this supply naturally stood a greater chance of survival than its fellows who could not. In view of this, it is not surprising to find that the majority of late Devonian fish had devised some means or other of utilising atmospheric oxygen.[176] The actinopterygian bony fish, the lobe-finned bony fish and even the weird-looking antiarchs all appear to have developed outgrowths from the pharynx that must have been able to act as lungs (Fig. 19a).[54] This clearly involved changes in the arterial arches but, as in the living lungfish, this entailed only an extra arterial branch developing from the last arterial arch. The actinopterygians eventually returned to the sea and their lungs lost their primary respiratory function to become hydrostatic organs; there is no real need for an accessory breathing organ in the sea, and such is the opportunism of evolution that a new role was quite quickly found for the air bladder. As far as air breathing was concerned, this was an attribute shared by most fish, allowing them to survive periods of drought and was an obvious advantage for any fish living in an environment subject to marked seasonal climatic changes.

If a lake or pool really begins to dry up, survival will not solely depend on the capacity to breathe air; unless the animal can aestivate, the only solution is for it to drag itself through the mud until it reaches the next pool. This however is easier said than done. No fish can swim over mud, and only those fish with fins having a bony axial skeleton to give leverage, so pushing the animal through the mud, will have much chance of survival in such circumstances. There were fish with such fins, coelacanths, rhipidistians and lungfish, although this type of fin did not originate for the purpose of helping the animals crawl about in mud. It so happened that this highly mobile fin, originally developed from a simple stabiliser, proved to be eminently suitable for grovelling in the mud. One of the notable features of the fins of the more advanced of these fishes is the foreshadowing of the bones of the tetrapod limb by their main skeletal elements. This is especially true of the pectoral fins, which are much more strongly developed than the pelvic, the exact reverse of the general rule in all land vertebrates. The reason for this apparent discrepancy is that the fins not only have to drag the body through the mud but also, as the animal must be able to continue breathing, must raise the head. If this were not done, the weight of the head would crush the gill region and it would be impossible for the animal to gulp air into its lungs.

The development of strong fins, enabling the fish to crawl slowly over the land, was not to allow them to conquer a new environment, but so that the animals could survive during a bad part of the year. With better times, they could continue to flourish as fish. Movement on land was always the last resort. So much for pioneering! Nevertheless these specialisations were the essential prerequisites for a future terrestrial existence. In fact these fish were preadapted for such a life.

'Choanichthyes'

In order to identify the group of lobe-finned fish that gave rise to the amphibians, it is necessary to examine certain minor details. One characteristic feature of the tetrapods is the choana, or third nostril. Generally in fish there are incurrent and excurrent ducts to the nasal organ, but the tetrapods have a third opening connecting the nasal sac with the pharynx; this opening is the choana, otherwise known as the internal nares or nostril. If any of the lobe-finned fish can be shown to possess a choana, then it is likely that the land vertebrates originated from this type. There were three major groups of lobe-finned fish, all at one time classified as Choanichthyes in the belief that they had a choana. Of these, the dipnoans or lungfish were favourite candidates for the ancestors of the tetrapods, as they had an internal nostril, or at least one opening into the mouth. There was, however, only *one* other, not the expected *three*. That the absence of the third was not appreciated for a long time is understandable, as the fish excurrent nostril is not over-conspicuous in the higher vertebrates, in which it survives as the naso-lachrymal duct. In the earliest lung-fish the so-called internal nostril is positioned at the margin of the mouth and not within it and hence must have gradually migrated into the oral cavity of the living forms during evolution.[90] This is a re-sited excurrent nostril and has nothing to do with a choana. The dipnoans can therefore be excluded from the direct ancestry of the tetrapods. In addition to this, the pattern of the skull roofing bones cannot be homologised with those of any tetrapod, or indeed with any other group of fish. From a primitive tessellated pattern in the earliest forms there evolved a pattern unique to the lungfish, now assigned to an independent class of the vertebrates.[91]

The other, crossopterygian, lobe-finned fish are divided into two separate groups, the coelacanths and the rhipidistians. In the living coelacanth *Latimeria* there is no sign of a choana, and this has been attributed to the adoption of a deep sea habitat, with the consequent irrelevance of such a structure. Their Devonian representatives were nevertheless assumed to have had one; but Jarvik has shown that they did not. So, although the pattern of the skull roofing bones would not exclude the coelacanths from tetrapod ancestry, the absence of a choana most certainly does.[91]

A choana was present, however, in the third and last group of the misnamed 'Choanichthyes', the rhipidistians, making them the only candidates for ancestors of the higher vertebrates. Twenty-five years ago, Jarvik[90] in a masterly exposition, claimed to show that within the rhipidistians two orders—the porolepidiformes and osteolepidiformes—represented the basic stocks of the urodele amphibians on the one hand, and the anurans and all the other higher vertebrates on the other. Jarvik's conclusions were based on serial sections through the snouts of his fossils. From the data he presented, it is evident that the snouts of porolepids and osteolepids were very different, and also that they appeared astonishingly similar to those of urodeles and anurans respectively (Fig. 20a, b, e, f). Jarvik concluded, reasonably enough, that the tetrapods were at least diphyletic in origin. The reaction to Jarvik's thesis was either uncritical acceptance or blank denial on the grounds that the living amphibians are obviously closely related to one another. Not until the last few years has anyone else examined the snouts of the rhipidistians. Thomson[230-3] has shown that the basis of Jarvik's work on the snout is suspect, as the differences he described appear to be a function of the length or breadth of the snout. Thomson has criticised Jarvik's approach for concentrating on minutiae of structures rather than on a broader canvas. However, it is only with a deep knowledge of the details of morphology that clues can be found to the real affinities of animals; broad similarities merely reflect comparable adaptations to similar conditions. In spite of the doubt shed on Jarvik's interpretation of the snout, his general conclusions have been received favourably by people working on urodeles, such as Fox.[63]

Although more than two decades elapsed before Jarvik was challenged in detail, he accumulated during this period still further evidence to support his thesis of the diphyletic origin of the tetrapods, and continued the serial sectioning of fossil skulls.[93,94,97] Whilst it may be possible to dismiss the interpretations of the snout as being simply a consequence of the different proportions in different genera, it is infinitely more difficult to dismiss the latest data presented by Jarvik.[93,94] The details of the floor of the mouth, the tongue and the hyobranchial skeleton all seem to point to a separate origin of the urodeles from all other higher vertebrates (Fig. 20c, d, g, h). It is to be hoped that this work will be tested before another twenty years have elapsed.

In the meantime, it must be conceded that Jarvik has amassed an impressive array of data which ought to be accepted on its merits until such time as contrary evidence is presented.

Recently Cox[41] has demonstrated that all the living amphibians, now termed the Lissamphibia, can be derived from the small lepospondyl amphibians, which in turn probably originated from the porolepids,

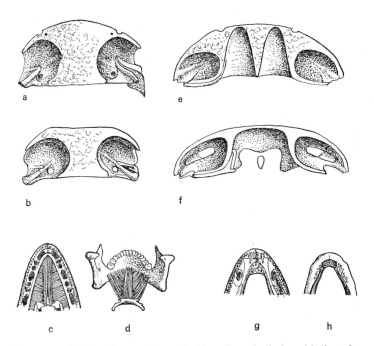

FIG. 20. a. Section of snout of osteolepid to show similarity with that of b. anuran (frog); c. floor of mouth of osteolepid compared with that of d. man; e. section of snout of porolepid to show similarity with that of f. urodele; g. floor of mouth of porolepid compared with that of h. urodele. (after Jarvik).

so automatically giving at least the living amphibians a monophyletic origin. The crux of the matter seems to be the status of the anurans: either they should not be associated with the higher tetrapods, as Jarvik[6,95] insists, an apparently reasonable view due to their highly specialised nature or, on the other hand, they are not lepospondyl descendants as Cox claims. There is a third possibility which should, however, not be over-stressed, that Jarvik's theory is correct, but that the living Amphibia, whilst still of diphyletic origin, retain most of the primitive features associated with the earliest tetrapods. These, when observed in the living forms in which all the soft parts are available for study, tend to stress their common inheritance.

The First Amphibian

Jarvik's theories, however regarded, suggest that there is every reason to believe that the tetrapods were, if not polyphyletic, certainly diphyletic. However, the rhipidistian fishes were not a very diverse group and in perhaps the majority of their features, but particularly their soft tissue anatomy, they were comparable. It must be remembered

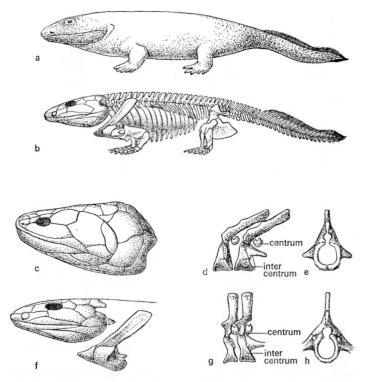

Fig. 21. *Ichthyostega*. a. Restoration; b. skeleton in lateral view; c. skull of osteolepid; d, e. vertebrae of osteolepid in lateral and anterior views; f. skull of *Ichthyostega*; g, h. vertebrae of *Ichthyostega* in lateral and anterior views. (after Jarvik).

that, as they were all living in the same type of habitat, selection could be expected to act on them in a similar way, so that evolution of the rhipidistians towards the amphibians' grade of organisation could be expected to have occurred on a broad front. In fact, if the main changes leading to the Amphibia were merely concerned with enabling fish to survive as fish, one would expect the first amphibians to have evolved during the Devonian period; and this is indeed the case. The first amphibian of which we have any adequate knowledge is *Ichthyostega* from the Upper Devonian of East Greenland (Fig. 21a, b).[91]

This animal in many ways straddles the boundary between fish and amphibian, but since greater emphasis is quite correctly placed on the

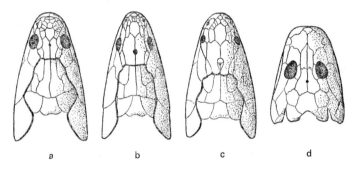

a   b   c   d

FIG. 22. Dorsal views of skulls to show gradual change in proportions, increase in length of snout, and reduction of skull table

a. *Osteolepis* (Middle Devonian); b. *Eusthenopteron* (Upper Devonian); c. *Eusthenodon* (Upper Devonian); d. *Ichthyostega*. (after Jarvik).

more advanced progressive features, it is classed as an amphibian. The relationship of the ichthyostegids to the osteolepids is in no doubt. The characters of their vertebrae are the same and the pattern of skull roofing bones is directly comparable (Fig. 21c–h). However, there are a number of significant differences in the relative proportions of these bones. The position of the parietals in *Ichthyostega* is further back, relative to the orbits, thus continuing a trend that can be followed within the rhipidistian fishes themselves. There is a progressive increase in the length of the snout and concomitant shortening of the posterior table of the skull (Fig. 22). This sequence of changes is the result of the gradual increase in the importance of the sense of smell of animals that are obliged to spend some time out of water. The increased olfactory powers were, in all probability, of prime survival value as they allowed the animal to locate on the wind the direction of the nearest open body of water, just as thirsting cattle can smell water from some considerable distance away. The hyomandibular became a sound conductor, again more sophisticated to pick up sound in air, and the spiracular cleft the otic notch. The limbs were sturdy and of typical pentadactyl type; however, they can easily be derived from those of the rhipidistians. The unusual shape of the humerus, for example, is due to the muscles that have their origins or insertions on it. In fact, there is no really fundamental change in its morphology from the rhipidistians to man, the same arrangement of muscles being retained throughout the higher vertebrates.

In two features the ichthyostegids remain fish-like. They were the only tetrapods to have retained some of the opercular bones which, admittedly reduced to vestiges, are nonetheless there. These animals also possessed a fish tail that had true fin rays, or lepidotrichia, on its dorsal fin. The genuine legs of these animals may seem a little odd for creatures that had no needs beyond surviving in a fishy world as fish. With stronger legs, however, their effective powers of travelling from pond to pond would have been enormously increased, so that during the dry season they would possess a great advantage over their more conservative relatives.

The Age of Amphibians

With the change in climatic conditions that marked the succeeding Carboniferous period, there were no problems of drought; far from it, there was water in abundance. Vast areas of the earth's surface were covered with swamps, in which giant ferns and mossess flourished, as well as myriads of insects. These conditions must have proved almost idyllic for the vertebrates of the time. Here, if anywhere, was the primeval Garden of Eden—paradise such as the world has never seen before or, for that matter, since. No longer were there seasonal droughts, when life must often have hung by the merest thread; now for twelve months in a year there was abundant food. The four-legged fish were well adapted to this new environment; they were able to scuttle through the shallow waters of the swamps, scramble across the mud and over fallen tree trunks with considerable ease. Their young, too, were well provided for by the aquatic larvae of the insects and other invertebrates living in the waters. As far as the amphibians were concerned, selection pressure was minimal. Virtually any type of vertebrate was viable, and the variety of amphibians that flourished included some very bizarre-looking animals. This new world provoked a rapid radiation of the amphibians. This phenomenon seems to confirm the view of many palaeontologists that major advances in evolution occur when natural selection is in abeyance.

Despite favourable conditions in the swamps of the Carboniferous, most of the amphibians quite independently exhibited similar evolutionary trends. In the circumstances in which they lived there was no incentive to leave the water, and with few exceptions they all became better adapted for an aquatic existence. The limbs became weaker and the bodies flatter. This was simply an adaptation to shallow waters; a flat animal slithering through shallow waters will obviously do better than a deep-bodied one.[14] Being squat is all very well as far as moving through the shallows is concerned, but it has one very great drawback: normally the skull is fixed rigidly to the vertebral column and when an animal bites or merely ingests its prey the lower jaw is closed. For this to be possible in these flat amphibians they would need either to stand on their legs to give room for the jaw to be lowered, or alternatively to rest with their heads over a hole, so that the same action could occur without standing up. Both these alternatives are, of course, absurd. There is another way of opening the mouth, simply by raising the skull without moving the lower jaw. An ichthyostegid or any other primitive amphibian was incapable of accomplishing this feat. As the joint between the skull and lower jaw was both behind and below its articulation with the vertebral column, the raising of the skull on the lower jaw would result in great stress on the anterior part of the rigid vertebral column. This problem was overcome by the gradual alignment of the two articulations into one plane (Fig. 23). The lower jaw developed a strong posterior process which was clearly for the attachments of muscles raising the skull. These changes, documented by Watson,[14] accompanied the flattening of the overall shape of the body, with the gradual reduction and weakening of the limbs. In fact, the main evolutionary trends in the amphibians were to improve their adaptations to life in shallow waters.

Even the frogs and toads, which are always considered to exemplify terrestrial vertebrates, evolved their specialised hind limbs, not for jumping on land but as efficient swimming organs. Griffith[71] has shown that the specialised nature of the anurans can be properly understood only as adaptations to an aquatic existence. The Triassic frog *Protobatrachus* seems to have been a large tadpole. Fully grown tadpoles have two swimming movements, spurts or kicks from the hind limbs and hovering movements by the tail. *Protobatrachus* had a flexible vertebral column, to which the sacrum was not fused, implying that the main swimming action was from the tail (the unfused nature of the sacrum tends to confirm the view that this specimen was a larva). When the main propulsive force is taken over by the hind limbs, it is necessary to eliminate any vertebral wobble, as can be done by shortening the column and by fusing the posterior vertebrae into a solid urostyle, thus

G

enabling the column to withstand shock. Griffith[71] has recorded impressions in mud of Permian age of frog hand-prints, which show that they were used for probing into the substratum, again confirming the primarily aquatic nature of the group. The early frogs swam like 'frog-men' using their fore limbs for manoeuvring and probing the mud for small invertebrates. Since frogs are frequently used to illustrate

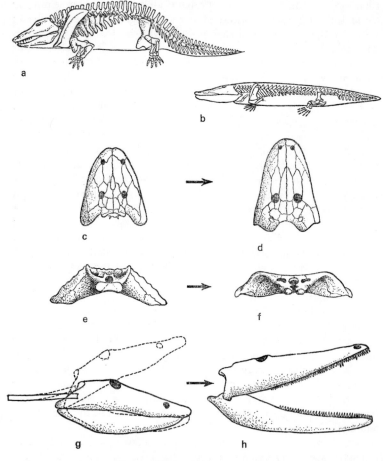

FIG. 23 a, c, e, g. *Eryops* (Carboniferous): a. skeleton, lateral view; c. skull, dorsal view; e. skull, posterior view; g. skull, lateral view to show difficulty in raising upper jaw; b, d, f, h. *Paracyclotosaurus* (Triassic); b. skeleton, lateral view; d. skull, dorsal view; f. skull, posterior view; h. skull, lateral view. (after Watson).

the metamorphosis from a fully aquatic larva to a terrestrial adult, they are often regarded as typical amphibians. It is, however, a travesty to consider them as such. They are in fact the most highly specialised of amphibians and perhaps even of the vertebrates.

The other important group of living amphibians that includes the newts and salamanders, the urodeles, also shows specialisations for an aquatic mode of life. The lepospondyls from which they arose were characterised by their reduction, and even complete loss, of limbs and the development of the tail as a swimming organ. The most renowned of urodeles, with the possible exception of *Homo diluvii testis* (recognised by Cuvier to be a fossil salamander), are the Mexican axolotls. These are neotenous salamanders that reproduce while still in the tadpole stage, and the story has it that when the savants returned to the Jardin des Plantes after the siege of Paris during the Franco-Prussian war of 1871, they found that the axolotls had all disappeared and that in their place were a lot of salamanders. Thus, reputedly, was the discovery made that under adverse conditions axolotls will metamorphose, but under normal conditions they remain permanently aquatic. Many urodeles, on the other hand, have lost this capacity and remain permanently neotenous.

The frogs and urodeles use their skin as a breathing organ and in some instances its importance may rival the lungs. However, the problem of desiccation arises and can become very real, as the skin must of necessity be porous if it is to act as a respiratory organ. Indeed, it is frequently suggested that in the transition from water to land animals must have acquired a waterproof skin to prevent excess water-loss from the body. This, however, was certainly no problem for the amphibians living in Carboniferous swamps. In any event, both the rhipidistian fish and the early amphibians possessed a heavy armour which would undoubtedly have acted, if required, as an effective proofing. Indeed it seems that this question of the dangers of desiccation did not arise until the skin had evolved into an accessory breathing organ. It appears to be an important problem only because of the assumption that the early amphibians must have had the same physiological requirements as their living descendants, an assumption that is clearly unwarranted.

'Eoreptilia'

The amphibians are frequently given the credit for making the great breakthrough in the transition from water to land. Nothing could be further from the truth; the main interest of any respectable amphibian during the Carboniferous was to stick to life in the wet. One group, the Eoreptilia of the Broughs,[27] which includes the microsaurs and embolomeres, was conspicuous in not conforming to these trends; they retained their deep fish-like bodies and skulls and did not reduce the strength of their limbs. These animals are distinguished from the ichthyostegids and other primitive amphibians by the form of their vertebrae.

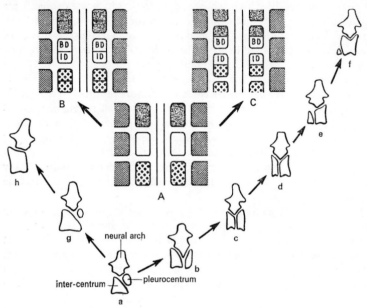

FIG. 24. A–C. Development of sclerotomes (stippled) and myotomes (hashured):

A. Early stage showing segmental arrangement; B. Sclerotomes divided into basidorsals and interdorsals, retaining segmental pattern; C. Sclerotomes divided and resegmented: a–h. *evolution of vertebrae in lateral view*: a. rhipidistian or primitive rhachitome; b–d. primitive to advanced embolomeres; e. seymouriamorph; f. primitive reptile; g. rhachitome; h. stereospondyl. (after Romer).

In the rhipidistians and ichthyostegids the main part of the vertebra was the intercentrum, the centrum or pleurocentrum formed two small crescent-shaped bones in front. This type of vertebra, termed rhachitomous, characterised the majority of the successful amphibians of the Carboniferous (Fig. 24g). In the advanced forms the centrum was reduced until it eventually disappeared. This stereospondylous type of vertebra developed quite independently in many different evolutionary lineages. In contrast, the centrum in the embolomeres became gradually larger until it equalled the intercentrum in size. Thereafter it continued to increase until the intercentrum was eventually reduced to the merest nubbin of bone. The main body of the embolomerous vertebra was formed by the centrum, a condition characterising the reptiles and higher vertebrates (Fig. 24b–f).[180] So far no explanation for these well documented changes has been proposed, but in recent years Shute[184] has provided a possible key. He has shown that the generally accepted view of the resegmentation of the vertebrae in fish and amphibians is wrong, in that the sclerotomes and myotomes actually retain their basic segmental nature. The anterior part of the sclerotome consists of the basidorsal and basiventral, the posterior of the interdorsal and interventral, so that the rhachitomous vertebra was segmental in origin, as also probably was the stereospondylous one. In the reptiles and mammals, on the other hand, the vertebrae are formed from the fusion of the posterior part of one sclerotome with the anterior part of the succeeding one (Fig. 24A–C). This means that the myosepta separating the myotomes are situated in the middle of the vertebrae, which thus become resegmented. The staggering of the musculature and the vertebrae had important consequences, as it made for great strength and more effective support. Whereas such staggering will have little value in an aquatic animal, where the musculature acts in unison throwing the body into sinuous waves, in a land vertebrate it will considerably increase the effectiveness of both the muscles and the vertebrae. Indeed the increase in the proportions of the centrum in the embolomeres appears to illustrate the gradual way in which this transition was accomplished.

The fully terrestrial condition is found in the most reptilian of the amphibians, the seymouriamorphs, the advanced Eoreptilia of the Broughs.[27] Indeed many of their skeletal characters were more reptilian than amphibian (Fig. 25). However, the pattern of skull roofing bones was the same as in the embolomeres. The articulation of the skull on the vertebral column was by a single occipital condyle, as in reptiles and unlike the double articulation of normal amphibians. Surprisingly, this single articulation is not an advanced feature but is merely the retention of a condition found in all primitive amphibians surviving from the rhipidistian stage. It is possible to think of the reptiles in this connection as more primitive than the amphibians; they have retained a condition that has greater potential for variable movement than the more specialised and rigid situation of the latter. In the earliest seymouriamorphs the number of phalanges was the same as in normal amphibians, but in later forms it increased to give the phalangeal formula 23454 which is characteristic of the reptiles.

With the sprawling gait of these animals, the increase in the length of the two outer digits ensured that the hands and feet had a firmer grip on the land. Similarly the sacrum is more developed; in amphibians the pelvic girdle articulates with one vertebra, in reptiles with at least two, and in the advanced seymouriamorphs with one—but a second was clearly becoming incorporated. The ilium had expanded dorsally,

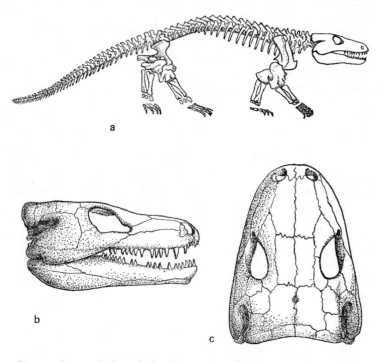

FIG. 25. *Seymouria* (Permian). a. Restoration of skeleton; b. skull, lateral view; c. skull, dorsal view. (after White).

indicating stronger development of the walking muscles. The orientation of the zygopophyses of the vertebrae in the horizontal, instead of at 45° as in the embolomeres, restricted movement of the vertebral column in the vertical plane, an important factor in a terrestrial animal and typical of the early reptiles. Overall the skeleton of the seymouriamorphs reveals a perfect transition from the amphibian to the reptilian condition. They are frequently considered to be, if not the first reptiles, then at least animals that straddle the boundary. Some popular works portray them laying shelled eggs and thus imply reptilian affinities! All the evidence would seem to point in this direction. Unfortunately *Seymouria* itself upsets this notion by retaining a lateral line system, found only in amphibians with an aquatic tadpole.

After virtually achieving reptilian status, at least as far as palaeontologists are concerned, they went the way of their contemporaries. The last seymouriamorph, *Kotlassia*, had weak limbs and a flat head and body like the majority of amphibians. In the final analysis the seymouriamorphs seem to have settled for the water; the inducements to move onto land were still insufficient.

8 : Early Reptiles

The origin of the reptiles presents an intractable problem, as by definition a reptile is distinguished from more primitive vertebrates by its mode of reproduction. Amphibian eggs are fertilised externally and are shed directly into the water, where the developing tadpoles have to fend for themselves. The reptilian egg, in contrast, is fertilised internally and then laid. This remarkable object allows the young to develop in its own private pond and with its own food supply, and has facilities for breathing and even a waste disposal unit! The development of this type of egg, the amniote or cleidoic egg, made possible the real conquest of the land, and must surely rank as one of the major breakthroughs in vertebrate history.

The Origin of the Amniote Egg

In this egg the developing embryo is surrounded by a number of membranes (Fig. 26). The amnion envelops the embryo enclosing it in a watery environment so cushioning it against any undue buffeting. The embryo rests on a yolk sac containing its food supply. A second membrane, the allantois, has an abundant vascular supply and acts as a lung, part also serving as a storage unit for waste products. The whole is enclosed in another membrane, the chorion, which comes to lie next to the shell and with it protects the egg from mechanical harm and yet is sufficiently porous to allow oxygen to diffuse in and carbon dioxide out. The advantages accruing from the possession of such an egg are obvious; environments formerly closed become available for habitation, so leading to vast opportunities for further evolution. Such indeed were the consequences of the appearance of the amniote egg, and it is frequently tacitly assumed that this is why it evolved. The only trouble is, as Romer[175] has stressed, that even when the first reptiles had acquired this new device freeing them from their reproductive tie to the water, they continued to spend generation after generation largely

92

slopping about in it. It is hard to believe that this egg was evolved to prepare the reptiles for the time when all the Carboniferous swamps dried up; such evolutionary foresight is plainly nonsensical. Since, having acquired an amniote egg, they were quite content to continue living amphibian lives, it must mean that this new method of reproduction had an advantage for the 'amphibian'.

The amniote egg must be laid on dry land; in fact it does no good at all to be laid at the bottom of a pond. It may seem odd that amphibians should find any advantage in such an egg. However, modern frogs,

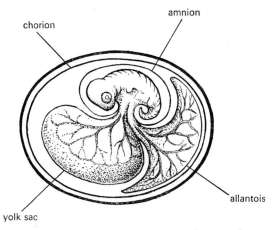

FIG. 26. Amniote or cleidoic egg to show various membranes.
(after Bystrow).

especially tropical ones, go to inordinate lengths to avoid laying their eggs in open bodies of water. Some lay their eggs under logs or stones, or in cavities in the earth, some even high in the trees in the small pockets of water that collect at the junction of branches with the trunk. The eggs of others develop in pockets in the skin of the mother's back, others in the father's vocal pouch, and in the case of the obstetrical toad, wrapped around the male's legs. In one instance, the eggs are laid in branches overhanging pools or streams, so that when the larvae hatch out they immediately drop into the water to swim away. As well as these devices there are also modifications of the eggs themselves. The typical amphibian egg has only a small yolk and except for the surrounding jelly there are no membranes or other protections for the embryo. This of course contrasts with the amniote egg with its large yolk and multiple membranes. However, in some living anurans the embryo develops on a large distended yolk sac so that the animal is provided with an adequate food supply during the most vulnerable period of its development. Even air-breathing is made possible by the growth of a highly vascular tail or of sheets of tissue from the gill region. Again, although no amnion is ever developed, in some cases the embryo is almost completely enclosed in a comparable sheet of tissue. In one way or another, every aspect of the amniote egg has its parallel in modern amphibians. In all the cases mentioned, these modifications of the normal developmental stages are connected not so much with enabling the animals concerned to be completely terrestrial, as with giving their offspring a better chance of life. In the conditions prevailing in the Carboniferous swamps it is easy to see how this would similarly apply.

With the advent of spring, probably milliards of eggs were laid in the water in the hope that a few would survive the carnage, the amphibians simply providing a prodigious free meal every year for practically everything from worms and insects to other amphibians. Not only was this a great waste of reproductive effort, but the tadpoles themselves, if they survived, would be in direct competition with one another. The development of the amniote egg would have conferred an immediate advantage for the amphibians, by removing the vulnerable egg to a relatively protected situation. Indeed here again is a structure that evolved for one purpose in one environment, which at the same time was the key to success in a quite different one. The animals with this mode of reproduction were highly successful amphibians, although reptiles by definition. Although it is not possible to determine the method of reproduction from the skeleton alone, and although fossils are classified as amphibian or reptile purely on their bones, it can nonetheless be shown that the amniote egg must have originated during the Carboniferous period. As both mammals and reptiles produce the amniote egg, it must have originated before these two major evolutionary lineages diverged. Since mammal-like reptiles are known from the Bashkirian stage (lower part of the Upper) of the Carboniferous,[20,30] this divergence must have occurred by this time, suggesting that the common ancestor of both lineages had already evolved this mode of reproduction. By definition, genuine reptiles lived the life of amphibians. In spite of this, their skeletons were more advanced than those of the amphibians, and they were capable of running with much greater agility than the latter. These reptiles, rather than slyly lying in wait in the shallows and slithering through the waters to engulf their prey with huge wide jaws, scampered over fallen tree trunks in a much more aggressive and active way. But, as the prey was not merely engulfed but may well have put up some sort of a struggle, it was vital for the jaws to be effectively braced to withstand the extra strain put on them.

Classification of Reptiles

This was accomplished by bringing the quadrate, the bone on which the lower jaw articulated, into the vertical plane (Fig. 27a–c). In the amphibians it slopes obliquely back, in the reptiles, at least the primitive ones, it is vertical. As Watson[241] has shown, there are basically two ways by which the quadrate could have become vertical, either by

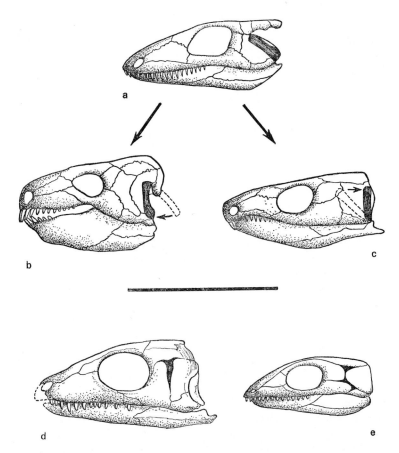

FIG. 27. Diagram to show alternative methods of bringing quadrate into vertical alignment: a. seymouriamorph; b. diadectomorph; c. captorhinomorph. d, e. origin of temporal openings: d. *Milleretta* (Permian) showing incipient development of temporal opening; e. diagram to show possible positions of temporal openings. (after Watson).

swinging forward from a fixed upper surface or the reverse. In the first case the otic notch and entire ear apparatus would be unaffected, but there would be some exaggeration of the notch. If, on the other hand, the quadrate were moved backwards with its lower end fixed, the otic notch would be eliminated and the tympanic membrane and auditory apparatus displaced. Both methods were used, leading to marked differences in the arrangement of the ear region.

This difference, although simply a consequence of improving the jaw mechanism, is of fundamental significance, since it divided the reptiles into two basic groups, one that led to the living reptiles and birds and the other that led to the mammals. Goodrich,[70] on the basis of the blood systems, divided the amniotes into two major groups, the Sauropsida including the majority of fossil, all the living reptiles and the birds, and the Theropsida including the mammal-like reptiles and mammals, whose arterial arches could not be derived one from another. Both types could, however, have originated from the system found in the amphibians. Goodrich recognised that there was a fundamental separation of the higher vertebrates, and his conclusions have been brilliantly confirmed by Watson, who analysed the ear region in the most primitive of the fossil reptiles and demonstrated that the division between the sauropsids and the theropsids was present when the reptiles made their first appearance. Watson concluded that they represented two separate evolutionary lines from the embolomerous amphibians.

With Watson's[241] theory as a guide, attempts have been made to classify such groups as the ichthyosaurs and plesiosaurs either as sauropsids or as theropsids. However, if the sauropsid and theropsid characters of each group are listed, then both the ichthyosaurs and the plesiosaurs seem to have a variable mixture. From this Kuhn-Schnyder[112] concluded that the extreme difficulty encountered in trying to fit these groups into Watson's scheme, could quite simply be explained on grounds of mutual incompatibility. He was able to demonstrate that the plesiosaurs and their allies brought the quadrate into the vertical in a rather different way from either the sauropsids or theropsids. The ear region was displaced posteriorly, indicating that this group of reptiles too must have had an independent origin from the amphibians. More recently still, Kuhn-Schnyder[113,115] has been able to show that the peculiar box-shaped mollusc-eating reptiles, the placodonts, which are classically associated with the plesiosaurs, can in no way be related and that in fact this group must also have had a separate origin. The ear region gives by far the most satisfactory basis on which to classify the reptiles; moreover it establishes beyond any doubt that there was more than one basic stock.

Temporal Openings

The taxonomy of the reptiles is based on quite different criteria, the position and number of the temporal openings in the skull.[16] The dorsal and lateral parts of the head are covered by skull roofing bones, beneath which the cranium encloses the brain. The space between the cranium and the bones of the temporal region, accommodates the jaw musculature. With the improvement of the jaw mechanism, there was naturally enough an increase in the volume of the musculature. Since the space available was limited, the only way to overcome the confinement of the muscles was to open up the solid encasement at the side of the head to form temporal openings, or alternatively to emarginate the roofing bones. In the early embryological development of the skull the dermal bones do not meet each other to form a sutured union. This is, for example, the reason for the great vulnerability of a human baby's head; there are triangular gaps or fontanelles where the bones meet. In a situation where the tissues underlying such bones are developing into muscles and not brain, it is easy to see than an increase in the musculature could prevent the bones from finally knitting together (Fig. 27d, e). The gap will remain because of the extra room demanded by the muscles. Such a gap is likely to develop only at a point where at least three bones join, since only here will there be any significant potential space. In the pattern of skull bones, which has remained essentially the same from the ichthyostegids to ourselves, there are a limited number of such triple junctions. Furthermore, since simple mechanical factors are involved, the appearance of comparable temporal openings does not necessarily mean that the animals concerned must be genetically related. However, since a classification based on temporal openings seems to be universally accepted, it is useful to examine these groupings to ascertain their validity.

The Anapsida which have no temporal openings include the living chelonians, although several groups, such as the terrapins, have the posterior and ventral edges of the temporal roofing bones emarginated. The other major division of the anapsids is the Cotylosauria, the so-called 'stem reptiles' (Fig. 27b, c). Naturally enough one would expect all primitive reptiles of whatever lineage to have no temporal openings, on the assumption that they evolved from amphibians. As already noted, these stem reptiles include the earliest sauropsids and theropsids. To unite these two fundamentally distinct groups in a single taxon tends to confuse rather than clarify the situation. It seems preferable, therefore, to abandon the term Anapsida altogether.

Those reptiles having a single opening bounded by the squamosal, postorbital and quadratojugal/jugal are classified as Synapsida (Fig. 28A).

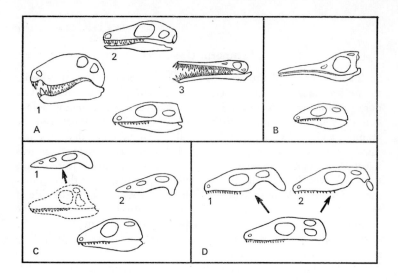

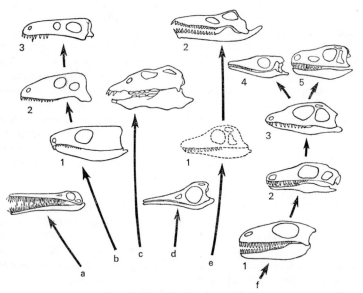

FIG. 28. Classification of reptiles

A. Synapsida: 1. paramammal, 2. millerosaur, 3. mesosaur; B. Parapsida:
ichthyosaur; C. Euryapsida: 1. plesiosaur, 2. placodont; D. Diapsida:
1. plesiosaur, 2. lizard.

a. Proganosauria (Mesosauria); b. Eotheropsida: 1. captorhinomorph,
2. pelycosaur, 3. therapsid; c. Placodontia; d. Ichthyopterygia;
e. Sauropterygia; f. Eusauropsida: 1. diadectomorph, 2. millerosaur,
3. eosuchian, 4. lizard, 5. archosaur.

The mammal-like reptiles are included in this subclass and, it must be admitted, do form a natural group, although their anapsid precursors should be associated with them. Apart from the fish-eating mesosaurs, which are apparently unrelated to any other group but have a synapsid opening, the Synapsida seemed to be a valid taxon. Unfortunately, this neat classification has been completely upset by Watson, who has shown that the millerosaurs, which have synapsid temporal openings, have at the same time sauropsid ears; these of course cannot be present in the mammal-like reptiles. The millerosaurs are the ancestors of the lizards and archosaurs, which have two temporal openings. Watson[241] has proved that these reptiles initially had only one temporal opening and developed the second one later. The first to evolve was the lower, which by definition makes these early sauropsids synapsids, so demonstrating the nonsense of the classification and the necessity of discarding the term Synapsida.

The third group, the Parapsida, have a single upper temporal opening, although this is formed at quite distinct bony junctions in the ichthyosaurs and sauropterygians (plesiosaurs and their allies) (Fig. 28B, C). The sauropterygians have the opening between the parietal, squamosal and post-orbital bones; the ichthyosaurs between the parietal, supratemporal and postfrontal. Since the temporal openings cannot possibly be homologous, the parapsids have long been separated into two subclasses, the term Parapsida being retained only for the ichthyosaurs. The sauropterygians are placed in the Euryapsida or Synaptosauria, characterised by its particular temporal opening. The situation in the ichthyosaurs is unique; but since the term Parapsida originally included the plesiosaurs as well, it is probably safer to discard the term to avoid any further confusion. The euryapsid situation is much more complex. Kuhn-Schnyder[113] has demonstrated that the placodonts, classically associated with the plesiosaurs, are in no way related. The only feature they have in common is an upper temporal opening. They both originated independently of one another from the amphibian grade of organisation. Furthermore, Kuhn-Schnyder[113,115] has recently suggested that the plesiosaurian condition actually arose from forms with two temporal openings in which the lower temporal bar was lost to produce a deep emargination of the lower border of the cheek bones. There are in addition a number of odd reptilian orders, united in the Araeoscelida, that have upper temporal openings and are hence classified as euryapsids, but cannot be confidently assigned to any of the other major groups. The term Euryapsida or Synaptosauria clearly refers to three major but probably unrelated lines, and hence should be dispensed with. The three groups of equal taxonomic rank are the Sauropterygia, Placodontia and Araeoscelida.

The Diapsida have, as the name implies, two temporal openings, a lower synapsid one between the squamosal, postorbital and quadrato-jugal/jugal and an upper euryapsid one between the squamosal, postorbital and parietal (Fig. 28D). With the exception of the possibly diapsid ancestor of the sauropterygians, this group is a perfectly natural one. Two major divisions are recognised, the lepidosaurs and the archosaurs. The latter retained two temporal openings throughout their history. In contrast, the lepidosaurs gradually eliminated the individual openings by breaking down the bony bars below them and forming a deep emargination of the lower border of the skull. The earliest lepidosaurs have either an anapsid or a synapsid skull, but in later ones—the ancestors of the true lizards—the skull was diapsid. This condition is still present in the tuatara, the rhynchocephalian lizard of New Zealand. The immediate precursors of true lizards had an incomplete lower temporal bar, but in later forms there is no sign of this lower boundary to the lower temporal opening. So the true lizards actually have only an upper temporal opening with a deep excavation at the lower margin of the cheek region. The articulation of the quadrate is modified to allow movement at its upper as well as lower end. This gives the jaws a much greater range of movement and is one of the reasons for the persistent success of this group from Triassic times. Towards the end of the Mesozoic the breakdown of the temporal bars continued in the snakes, which evolved from the lizards; the bar formed by the postorbital and squamosal was lost, so that strictly speaking there were no temporal openings at all. This change also resulted in the further improvement of the jaw mechanism, and in the advanced snakes even the postorbital bar is lost. The capacity of these reptiles to engulf prey of much larger girth than themselves, an obvious example being the boa-constrictor which can eat pigs or goats, depends on the freedom of jaw movement made possible by these changes. However, the fact that the most abundant and successful of all the living reptiles are not diapsid, although clearly diapsid derivatives, again stresses the inappropriateness of the term.

The living reptiles are classified into three groups: the anapsid chelonians, the diapsid lepidosaurs, and the archosaurs. On the same basis, the mammals could be considered as surviving synapsids. Although perfectly adequate for living forms, the classification based on temporal openings collapses when the fossil types are taken into account. Since this classification should no longer be accepted and the simple division into sauropsids and theropsids is also insufficient, it is necessary to introduce a new classification that at least approximates to the scheme of relationships now established. Just as the term 'Pisces' is now recognised as including a number of genetically unrelated classes of vertebrate, the Reptilia should be thought of as a superclass representing a particular structural grade of the higher vertebrates. This concept was expressed by Goodrich[70] in 1916: 'The group Reptilia represents not a true monophyletic class like the class Mammalia (*sic*) and the class Aves, but rather an assemblage or grade of Amniotes retaining a more primitive general structure.' Again as with the fish, the major phyletic groups warrant the taxonomic rank of separate classes. The classification which seems best to fit the facts now known is given below (Fig. 28a–f). Unfortunately it necessitates the introduction of several new terms. This is much regretted but is probably preferable to retaining old terms with radically new definitions, an unsatisfactory and confusing compromise.

A New Classification

SUPERCLASS REPTILIA

Class: Eusauropsida (including the sauropsid cotylosaurs, Chelonia, Lepidosauria and Archosauria) (Fig. 28f)

Class: Ichthyopterygia (Fig. 28d)

Class: Sauropterygia (including only the plesiosaurs and their allies the nothosaurs) (Fig. 28e)

Class: Placodontia (Fig. 28c)

Class: Proganosauria (Mesosauria) (Fig. 28a)

Class: Araeoscelida (for Araeoscelidia, Trilophosauria, and Proto-rosauria)

Class: Eotheropsida (including the theropsid cotylosaurs and Paramammalia—the 'mammal-like reptiles' or 'Synapsida' of other authors) (Fig. 28b)

This method of arranging the main groups of reptiles differs radically from that normally used, and should be justified by some discussion of the basis on which the vertebrates are classified. The major taxonomic divisions are based on one or other of two diametrically opposed beliefs. One view, the classical, holds that the reptiles were monophyletic in origin, the other that they were polyphyletic. According to the first view, all the reptiles are regarded as having evolved from a basal primitive stock presumably derived from advanced embolomeres which after achieving reptilian status experienced a rapid radiation. There is a deeply entrenched belief among many zoologists that the recognition of a major taxonomic unit represents, by definition, a group of animals with their common ancestor a member of the same taxon. This is perhaps a manifestation of the 'Adam and Eve Complex', in

H

which every evolutionary lineage began with an original pair—nowadays a species. This moreover involves the tacit assumption that major changes are confined to the occasional favoured lineage, whereas the lesson of the fossil record is the reverse. Where an adaptive advantage is conferred by a change in structure, this is found in the majority of contemporary forms.

Evolution occurs on a broad front, rarely if ever in the odd favoured line; identical structural modifications occur in quite unrelated groups. Major advances, no matter how strange seeming, appear not to have been unique events. The erection of arbitrary divisions among a series of animals evolving on a broad front is exceptionally difficult. As it is preferable to have a system of classification reflecting a genetic relationship, the criteria on which major divisions are based must be selected with the greatest care. Naturally enough those changes that are firmly believed to have occurred only once are most often espoused. A classification erected in this way is both phyletic and yet incorporates the concept of monophyly. However the fact that time and time again more than one lineage crossed the boundaries erected between the major groups of vertebrates, must alter our conception of the main vertebrate 'Classes'. They cannot be considered to represent genetically homogeneous assemblages. If they are not indicative of phylogenetic connections, should they be discarded? Such a course of action would be logical if it is insisted that a classification must be primarily phyletic. No such difficulty arose before the principle of evolution was established; the vertebrates were organised into groups reflecting different grades of structural organisation. The mammals and the birds are not directly related, but in the course of the evolution both have passed through a reptilian stage. Such a stage was reached by many lineages, some continuing their evolution further. The nomen Reptilia is therefore valuable as denoting a morphological state and can be retained on that basis, and without genetic overtones, as a convenient division of the vertebrates. With the possible exception of the birds, all the vertebrate classes are phyletically heterogeneous. This is no reason for discarding them; they retain their usefulness as major grades of organisation within the subphylum.

9 : Mammal-like Reptiles

The end of the Carboniferous was marked by a dramatic change in the earth's climate. The lush swamps dried up and were replaced by areas of desert and near-desert, and new mountain ranges formed. Instead of enjoying an environment offering ample food and little competition to the large numbers of amphibians and reptiles living an aquatic or semiaquatic life in the swamps, such vertebrates as survived were restricted to the small areas of the few remaining lakes and to the rivers. This change proved cataclysmic for most of the amphibians as only a few survived it, but provoked a successful radiation of the mammal-like reptiles or paramammals. This group had evolved from their immediate predecessors, the captorhinomorphs, during the Carboniferous but became the dominant element in the fauna only in the Permian, later to be overshadowed by the ruling reptiles of the Mesozoic. The paramammals are distinguished mainly by their lower or synapsid temporal opening. This group is divided into the primitive Pelycosauria of the Upper Carboniferous and Lower Permian (best known from the Texas Red Beds) and their successors, the more advanced Therapsida (not to be confused with Theropsida) of the Upper Permian and Triassic of the South African Karroo. The former are distinguished by their sprawling gait and undifferentiated teeth. During the evolution of the latter, the gait became mammalian, the dentition differentiated and the vertebral column flexed, so raising the head. The gradual evolution of the paramammals towards the mammalian condition can be traced in fossils from both Texas and the Karroo.

There is a gap in the geological record between the sequences in Texas and the Karroo, as obviously evolution continued during this missing period, and there is also a zoological gap between the pelycosaurs and the therapsids. This means that a firm taxonomic boundary can easily be drawn between these two groups of paramammals. Since this classification was established, the large and important Russian faunas have been described, from rocks spanning the geological hiatus, but—more important—the fossils themselves link the pelycosaurs and the therapsids. There is now a satisfactory sequence from the captorhinomorphs to the mammals. Although excellent as far as tracing the evolution of the eotheropsids is concerned, this creates considerable complications with regard to the classification. There is now no clearly defined boundary, but a continuum of gradual change. This latter, of course, more closely reflects the reality of the situation. Indeed the Russian 'missing links' are a subject of controversy, since authors find it difficult to decide into which groups the various forms should be assigned; the really significant point is that they show how the pelycosaurs grade into the therapsids.[145]

The Distribution of Paramammals

This distribution of these first truly terrestrial vertebrates is of some significance. The mammal-like reptiles were capable only of travelling over-land and, as they are found in widely separated provinces, it can be inferred that during Carboniferous, Permian and Triassic times these regions were connected. The same types of primitive eotheropsids are found from the late Carboniferous and early Permian of Texas and Western Europe, from where they spread into Russia. This suggests that North America and Europe were in close juxtaposition and that the Atlantic ocean had not yet formed. The detailed succession of faunas in Russia and the Karroo are so similar that geologists can accurately correlate the rocks of both sequences using the same fossil groups as zones. Clearly there was continual faunal interchange between these two provinces. This presupposes some sort of connection between the northern and southern continents despite the presence of the great ocean Tethys supposedly separating them. Somehow or other this seemingly impassable barrier was overcome not only once but time and time again. A possible explanation comes from the observations of Thaler[229] who has described dinosaur footprints in dolomitic rocks previously thought to have been deposited in deep water. Perhaps the great ocean of Tethys, so prominent on palaeogeographical maps was more apparent than real. It is interesting, however, that land animals could walk on the water but seemed quite incapable of walking on the land in either an eastern or a western direction.[76] They could not travel to South America or Australia. It has long been thought that South Africa, South America, India, Australasia and Antarctica were at this time united in the supercontinent of Gondwanaland. If so, it would be reasonable to expect the vertebrates to have been distributed throughout this huge land mass. In fact this did not happen, suggesting that Gondwanaland as a single continent did not exist. It must be conceded, however, that Bonaparte[23] has provided convincing evidence of some faunal interchange between Argentina and the Karroo in the late Triassic. This was at a time when comparable faunas had a world-wide distribution, so that there is still the possibility that the animals concerned travelled via the northern continents. As Haughton[76] has emphasised, it is a singular fact that there seems to have been continual faunal interchange across Tethys from Russia to the Karroo and virtually none across Gondwanaland!

The Achievement of Mammalian Status

During the radiation of the paramammals the first plant-eating vertebrates made their appearance. This was a major innovation and one which finally assured their success on dry and vegetation-covered land. Perhaps the most striking feature of the mammal-like reptiles as a whole is that every one of the many groups that evolved exhibited similar changes in structure, all of which lead towards mammalian status. These changes did not occur in the same order, however, or at the same rate in the different groups. Rather than give a systematic account of the different groups, it would seem more useful to discuss some of these changes and the possible reasons for them.

The earliest paramammals are found in Carboniferous rocks of Nova Scotia, preserved in hollow tree stumps.[30] From their numerous sharply pointed teeth it is evident that they were aquatic or semi-aquatic with a diet of fish. So even when the Carboniferous swamps dried up these animals were mainly to be found near lakes or streams rather than in inland regions. The most primitive of the paramammals had one or two teeth near the front of the maxillary tooth row that were slightly larger than those in the rest of the dentition. Watson[14] has shown that the gradual increase in the size of these anterior teeth can be traced until in the advanced pelycosaurs they became large stabbing and slashing canines (Fig. 29a–d). This indicates the gradual dietary transition from fish to meat, and again shows the continuation of the trend away from undue dependence on the water. As the height of the crowns of these teeth increased, there was a concomitant increase in the length of their roots. In order to accommodate the larger roots, the bone in which they are enclosed must be deepened. One of the characteristic trends that is observed in this group is the progressive deepening of the maxilla.

There is a further consequence of this change. The bones forming the roof of the mouth and perforated anteriorly by the internal nostrils, were firmly fixed both fore and aft as well as being connected to the maxilla. With the deepening of the maxilla, the roof of the mouth became strongly arched. This had the advantage of improving the mechanical strength of this part of the skull, and heralded a major structural change in the palatal region. The transverse arching of the palate allowed breathing to continue even when the animal was holding its prey in its mouth. The ability to breathe and simultaneously grasp and then gulp their prey gave the paramammals a distinct advantage. As the group evolved, this primitive arrangement was gradually improved; the

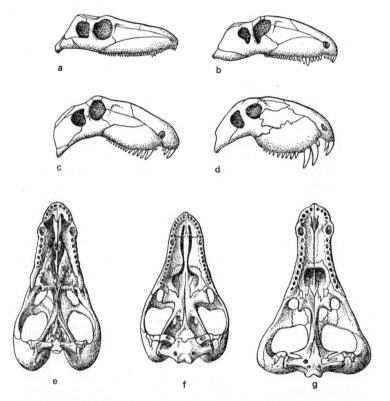

FIG. 29. a–d. Pelycosaurs showing increase in caniniform teeth with concomitant deepening of maxilla: a. *Varanosaurus*; b. *Ophiacodon*; c. *Sphenacodon*; d. *Dimetrodon*.

e–g. Therapsids showing development of secondary palate: e. *Sauroctonus*, with internal nares opening at posterior end of sloping groove, inferred presence of soft palate; f. *Procynosuchus*, median growth of maxillae and palatine bones into soft palate to form hard palate; g. *Cynognathus*, with fully developed hard palate. (after Watson and Bystrow).

internal nostril, opening further posteriorly as a flap of soft tissue, is thought to have covered the internal opening which was situated at the posterior end of the backward sloping groove. In the next stage, bony flanges grew from the palatine and maxillae to transform the soft palate into a hard one (Fig. 29e–g). Thus the air and food passages in the mouth became separated, so producing the characteristic secondary palate of the mammals. This development meant that the animal could maintain a continual supply of oxygen and with it a constant metabolic rate, a prerequisite for warm-bloodedness. With an homoiothermic metabolism and the complete separation of the food and air passages, due to the development of the secondary palate extending as far back as the posterior teeth, food could be retained in the mouth for a longer period and partially prepared for digestion. To do this, some elaboration of the posterior teeth into cutting and grinding organs was required, and in fact this occurred with the evolution of multicuspid cheek teeth in the most advanced therapsids.

These changes did not take place in isolation; the means of locomotion showed comparable advances. The early paramammals, with the limbs sticking out from the sides of the body, had the sprawling gait of primitive reptiles. Although slow and clumsy by modern standards, these animals were very stable. However, to be an efficient hunter, or for that matter to escape from a predator, rapidity of movement is advantageous. This can be accomplished if the limds are straight and close to the body, forming vertical struts, so that longer and more effective strides can be taken. This change was accompanied by changes in the pelvic girdle. In the early forms the ilium was a broad blade, expanded posteriorly and adapted for holding the femur firmly but horizontally from the body. With subsequent evolution the anterior part expanded, implying an important muscular component pulling the femur forwards (Fig. 30a–d). Ultimately the ilium lost its posterior extension, becoming a narrow anteriorly directed blade, the ischium forming a compensatory posterior one.[120] This type of pelvic girdle is associated with a forwards and backwards movement of the femur. With the development of the pelvic girdle, the femur itself underwent a sequence of changes which Parrington[155] has shown culminated in the articular head being placed laterally so that the femora became virtually perpendicular to the pelvic girdle instead of projecting laterally. This arrangement is essentially mammalian. However, the body lost its stability, but to counteract this there was a concomitant increase in the parts of the brain concerned with muscular coordination (Fig. 30e–h)—the cerebellum and the cerebral hemispheres. As the limbs raised the animal farther from the ground, there was at the same time a modification of the anterior part of the vertebral column to form a neck.

Whilst allowing the animals to feed from the ground, it also enabled them to take in much more of their surroundings. The correlation between what the animals observed and what they did must have been a major impetus leading to the achievement of true mammalian status.[120]

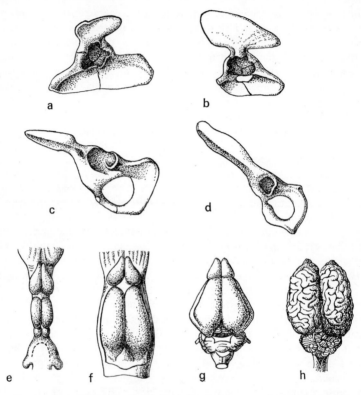

FIG. 30. a–d. Evolution of pelvic girdle showing anterior production of ilium (anterior to left):
a. *Dimetrodon*, a pelycosaur; b. *Cynidiognathus*, a therapsid; c. *Oligokyphus*, an advanced therapsid; d. *Didelphis*, a living marsupial;
e–h. evolution of brains, e. advanced therapsid; f. Jurassic mammal; g. tree shrew; h. horse. (after Lessertisseur and Sigogneau).

Mammals are conventionally recognised by their possession of fur or hair and, as the name implies, also of mammary glands used in suckling the young, indicating a measure of parental care. Possession of fur is associated with warm-bloodedness. The advanced para-mammals had turbinal bones in the nasal passages, and it is known that their function is to support the convolutions of the mucous membranes which warm the inhaled air. As these animals also had a fully mammalian secondary palate, it seems safe to conclude that they were warm-blooded. There is evidence from pits in the maxillae that the more advanced forms may have had vibrissae or whiskers, in view

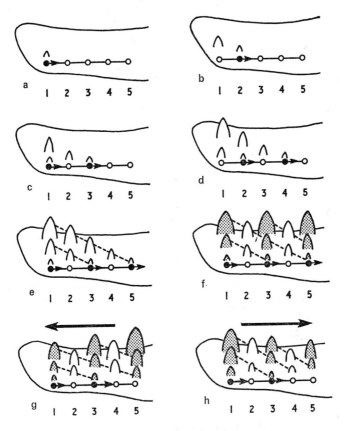

FIG. 31. Rhythms of tooth replacement

a. first 'impulse' induces formation of first tooth germ bud from dental lamina; b. impulse continues along lamina to second tooth position while first tooth germ continues to develop; c. second impulse begins journey; d. both impulses moving along lamina; e. third impulse begins and the dentition begins to appear; f. after a sequence of impulses, two tooth positions apart, have been passing along the dental lamina a completely alternate replacement pattern is produced; g. with the impulses $2\frac{1}{2}$ positions apart, the wave of replacement passes from back to front; h. with $1\frac{1}{2}$ positions apart, from front to back. (after Tarlo and Tarlo).

of which it can perhaps be suggested that they could have had fur or hair as well.

The evidence that the advanced paramammals suckled their young is much more indirect. All reptiles and the majority of mammal-like reptiles have a continual succession of teeth throughout their lives, with waves of replacement passing from the back of the jaw to the front. There was a sudden change in the most advanced paramammals and primitive mammals, the wave of replacement passing from front to back and the number of generations severely reduced. There was no satisfactory explanation for this dramatic change until Edmund[57] produced his analysis in 1960. He showed that the whole system behaves as if a stimulus passes along the dental lamina from front to back and that when it reaches a tooth position it induces the production of a tooth bud. He has further demonstrated that the different patterns of tooth replacement depend simply on the timing of the succession of 'impulses'. If successive impulses are two tooth positions apart, the pattern of replacement is exactly alternating, as in the sharks. With a slight difference in timing, if the distance is greater than two, e.g. $2\frac{1}{2}$, the replacement will be from back to front; on the other hand, if the distance between impulses is less than two, say $1\frac{1}{2}$, the wave of replacement will be from front to back (Fig. 31). This means that there is no longer any difficulty in deriving the mammalian pattern from the reptilian, but it does not solve the problem of the drastic reduction of generations and the general slowing down of tooth eruption in the mammals.[85] A young reptile on hatching has to have a fully functional dentition, as it has immediately to fend for itself. If, on the other hand, the young are suckled, it is an obvious disadvantage for the mother if they possess a functional dentition. It is therefore possible, to conclude, with a certain amount of justification, that the paramammals with a mammalian tooth replacement pattern probably suckled their offspring.

The Reptile-Mammal Boundary

In all the features that can be either observed or inferred in the mammal-like reptiles, there was a gradual approach to the mammalian condition. It is evident that the more advanced forms, being warm-blooded, furry, with an heterodont dentition, mammalian gait and breast-feeding, if alive today, would be unhesitatingly recognised as mammalian. Nevertheless, since the earlier forms appear just as incontrovertibly reptilian, it is insisted that a dividing line be drawn. In many respects this method of dividing the theropsids is ill-conceived. There was a gradual transition to the mammalian grade, which can be followed in almost every group of the Paramammalia. Once again the chosen boundary is one that, it was believed, could by the nature of things have been crossed only once—a 'unique' event. The change in the jaw articulation from the reptilian quadrate-articular to the mammalian squamosal-dentary, with the incorporation of the bones of the reptilian joint into the middle ear (Fig. 32a–d).

This change-over raises the problem of how the reptilian jaw joints became progressively reduced, as they undoubtedly did during the history of the paramammals, and at the same time continued to function

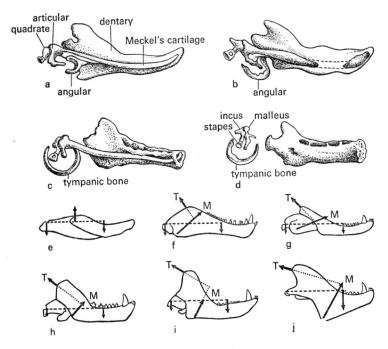

FIG. 32. a–d. Embryological development of mammalian jaws showing transformation of jaw elements into ear ossicles:

a. *Didelphis*, opossum; b. *Erinaceus*, hedgehog; c, d. *Homo sapiens*; e–j. evolution of jaw musculature with increase in power of bite and reduction of force at articulation: e. primitive pelycosaur with undifferentiated Capiti Mandibularis muscle; f. advanced pelycosaur with muscle in two major components, Superficial Masseter and Temporalis; g–i. therapsids showing progressive change in pull and alignment of Masseter and Temporalis; j. primitive mammal, *Diarthrognathus*, with strong bite and no force exerted at reptilian jaw articulation. T. line of action of Temporalis muscle; M. line of action of Superficial Masseter. (after Bystrow and Crompton).

efficiently. In the most advanced forms the quadrate and articular are reduced to mere nubbins. Crompton[43,44] has provided the solution to this paradox by showing that changes in the joint were preceded by differentiation and realignment of the muscles of mastication. The jaw musculature of the early reptiles acted to close the jaws on the hinge of the joint. This subsequently divided into two parts, the Temporalis and Masseter, which became progressively more antagonistic in their effects on contraction as the evolution of the jaws continued (Fig. 32e–j). Ultimately a state was reached where the functioning of the jaws was accomplished entirely by the muscles, giving a more effective bite and reducing the forces acting on the joint to a minimum. It followed that, as the loading on the joint decreased with the developing antagonism of the Temporalis and Masseter, the quadrate and articular would be reduced. Crompton[42] and Kermack[103,104] have in fact described two quite unrelated animals *Diarthrognathus* and *Morganucodon* which independently acquired the mammalian jaw articulation. This carefully defined boundary separating mammals from reptiles has been crossed not by a single favoured lineage but by at least four. The acquisition of the mammalian squamosal-dentary joint does not imply the instantaneous transformation of articular and quadrate into a sound-transmitting mechanism. However, Watson[14] has demonstrated that these two bones must have been floating free in the region of the tympanic cavity during the embryological development of the animal. It is not so much a question of how they became incorporated into the ear apparatus, but rather how they could possibly have avoided such a fate; Hopson[84] has given cogent functional reasons for this incorporation.

Evolution of Terrestrial Food Chains

By the end of the Triassic period several groups of paramammal had achieved full mammalian status, whatever the criteria used, and had become fully adapted to life on dry land. At the same time as they evolved towards mammalian status, the mammal-like reptiles became involved in the establishment of the modern terrestrial food chain, allowing them to become completely land-based. The evolution of this food chain has been worked out by Olson.[144,146] The clue to this evolution stems from the fact that in all the early faunas there was a predominance of carnivores. At first, this was thought to be one of the vagaries of the fossil record and that for some reason the herbivores had not been preserved. However, when the faunas of both North America and Russia were studied, it was found that the proportion of carnivores to herbivores was reasonably constant; the majority of

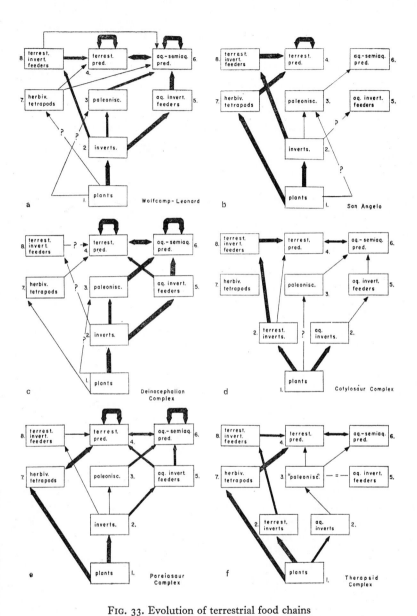

FIG. 33. Evolution of terrestrial food chains

a. Early Permian of North America; b. Upper Permian of North America; c. Upper Permian of Russia; (compare with a.); d. Upper Permian of Russia (contemporary with c.); e. late Upper Permian of Russia and South Africa; f. Lower Triassic of South Africa. (from Olson 1961).

animals were carnivores. This could no longer be explained away on the grounds of a geological bias in preservation. There had to be some other explanation for this apparent anomaly, since it is always assumed that there will be a preponderance of herbivores and a comparatively small number of carnivores preying on them. As previously noted, the earliest theropsids, the captorhinomorphs and paramammals, were semiaquatic feeders, living on fish, amphibians and their own kind; the smaller forms undoubtedly fed on aquatic invertebrates and in their turn were fed upon by their larger relatives. A few forms fed on terrestrial invertebrates, and these would have been preyed on by the more terrestrial of the larger predators. The energy flow was from plants to invertebrates, and thereafter to the vertebrates which were exclusively meat- or fish-eaters (Fig. 33a). Towards the end of the Texan sequence, a fully terrestrial food chain had developed. Here the vertebrates had started to eat the vegetation, and the herbivores thus provided a useful food supply for the carnivores, but only to the same extent as the terrestrial invertebrate-feeders did (Fig. 33b). Furthermore, the terrestrial predators still preyed on one another. In Russia the first totally land based food chain was devoid of herbivores (Fig. 33d). Here the main energy flow was from plants to terrestrial invertebrates, thence to invertebrate-feeders and eventually to terrestrial predators. Towards the end of the Permian period, the energy flow was from plants to vertebrate herbivores and then to the carnivores. However, these latter still fed off each other (Fig. 33e). Not until the dawn of the Triassic period was this particular habit discarded and what is considered to be the normal food chain established, with a preponderance of herbivores, a proportion of invertebrate-feeders, and a minority of carnivores feeding upon them but not on one another (Fig. 33f).

The mammal-like reptiles finally conquered the land, and no longer depended on water for their food or for their reproduction. Moreover, along with the development of many mammalian characters, their powers of locomotion had evolved, giving them a high degree of mobility. Although apparently poised for a successful radiation, the mammal-like reptiles were almost eclipsed by the rise of the sauropsids. They do not seem to have been able even to compete with the lizards for occupancy of the ecological niche of invertebrate-feeders; fortunately their homoiothermal metabolism allowed them to flourish during the long cold night of the Mesozoic era.

10 : Lizard *Inter-regnum*

While the paramammals were expending their evolutionary energy in mastering the continents, the eusauropsids were also evolving. These small lizard-like animals fed on insects and other invertebrates, and in turn were eaten by the carnivorous mammal-like reptiles. They were many and small and must have played an important role near the base of the food chain of the times. They underwent few evolutionary changes, but did develop temporal openings. The lower opening, the synapsid, was developed first and then the upper one, the euryapsid, making these animals, by definition, diapsid. In the lower Triassic period one major line began to reduce the lower temporal bar, and by the middle of the Trias there was an abundance of true lizards. Rather than competing directly with the mammal-like reptiles, they seem to have been shore-dwellers, either fish-eaters or littoral scavengers. In this sphere they did remarkably well. *Askeptosaurus*, with its deep swimming tail,[161] was adapted to a marine life. *Tanystropheus* evolved an incredibly elongated neck and was clearly specialised for something akin to clearing out drains (Fig. 34c); a number of fairly unspecialised and generalised lizards were also present.[110,111] Rhynchocephalian lizards still surviving in New Zealand, had developed by the beginning of the Trias, but during the middle and late Trias they gave rise to an enormously successful group of animals, the rhynchosaurs, which had a world-wide distribution (Fig. 34e–g).[178] These lizards were fully terrestrial and had powerful crushing jaws for cracking open the seeds of seed-fern, cycads and ginkgos, their teeth being ideal for coping with the thick hard shell or sarcotesta.

By the end of the Triassic period the lizard radiation was still under way, but the true lizards were well established on land. Unfortunately, for the fossil record, they flourished in the hills, and this, coupled with their smallness, has meant that few were preserved. Upland areas are regions that provide sediment; they are not places where sediment accumulates. Therefore, animals inhabiting such regions

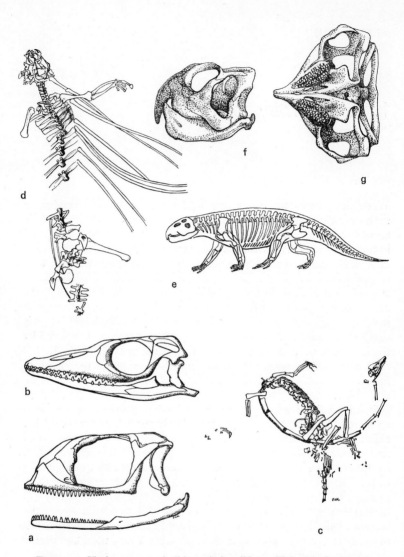

FIG. 34. a. *Kuehneosaurus*, skull lateral view (Upper Triassic); b. *Macrocnemus*, skull lateral view (Middle Triassic); c. skeleton of *Tanystropheus* (Middle Triassic); d. skeleton of gliding lizard *Icarosaurus* (Upper Triassic); e–g. rhynchosaur: e. restoration; f, g. skull in lateral and ventral views (Middle Triassic). (after Kuhn–Schnyder, Robinson, Colbert and Romer).

are almost guaranteed to be missing from the geological record. There is, however, one chance of finding them. If the region is composed of limestone rocks, caves and fissures will be formed in the ground, because the carbonic acid in rainwater is sufficient to dissolve the calcium carbonate of the limestone. Animals inhabiting caves and hollows may be preserved there, or bodies of animals may be washed into them. In either event their remains will stand a good chance of fossilisation. For the process to be completed, it is necessary for the region to be engulfed by the sea sufficiently rapidly to allow no time for the hills to be eroded away. If all these conditions are fulfilled, the occasional glimpse of life on the land away from the normal areas of deposition, such as estuaries, swamps and flood plains, will be preserved. As can be imagined, such freaks of preservation are not of common occurrence. There is such a deposit of middle Triassic age known in south west Poland, where, during this period, there was a string of islands across the straits separating the north German sea from the ocean of Tethys.[212,216] These islands were formed of Devonian limestone, and in the island of Gliny a system of caves and fissures developed. Along the floors of the caves there accumulated the bones of animals that lived there and also the remains of their food. Since this was an island, there are many bones of fish-eating reptiles as well as of fish, but also there are remains of lizards entirely modern in character. A comparable series of deposits are known from Britain; these are of Upper Triassic age and occur in Carboniferous limestones. Swinton[206] described a small rhynchocephalian lizard from a fissure, and since that time Kermack[102-4] and Robinson[171,172] have exploited these deposits, and have described small mammals and two further lizards. Although there are several other, as yet undescribed, lizards in this fauna, the importance of the two described genera, *Kuehneosuchus* ('*Plesiodraco*') and *Kuehneosaurus*, is that they establish the remarkable extent of the lizard radiation during this period.[172,216] Both these forms were gliding lizards, with enormously developed ribs which supported the gliding membrane. Another such lizard *Icarosaurus* has recently been described from the Upper Trias of New Jersey; which further indicates the great success of these animals (Fig. 34a, d).[39] This radiation, known only as a result of the discovery of fissure and cave deposits, is still not documented in detail. However, the extremes of specialisation already recorded prove that it must have been an important event in the evolution of the vertebrates. These lizards managed to colonise a wider variety of environments than the mammal-like reptiles. It may be significant that the rise of the lizards coincided with the beginning of the decline of the paramammals.

Although it must have seemed, during the latter part of the Triassic,

J

that the lizards were likely to replace the mammals as the dominant land vertebrates, this did not happen; the Age of the dinosaurs dawned and the brief radiation of the lizards came to an abrupt end. However, they were able to survive throughout the age of dinosaurs, filling the role of the feeders on small invertebrates. Although the more extreme specialised forms were unable to compete against other groups of reptiles that ousted them from their particular ecological niches, the small generalised types seemed to have gone on from strength to strength. Hoffstetter[82] has established that all the major superfamilies of living lizard were already in existence by the end of the succeeding geological period. In fact the lizard faunas acquired their modern characteristics quite early in the Mesozoic—the lizards of the Jurassic would have looked familiar to any herpetologist. During the Cretaceous period one group of varanid lizards returned to the sea, while a further group gave rise to the snakes. From the end of the Triassic period up to the present day the lizards have evolved and radiated with great success. Admittedly their advance has been of a modest nature, but proof of it is clearly to be seen in their great numbers and variety in tropical regions at the present day.

11 : Age of Dinosaurs

The Age of dinosaurs lasted for a hundred million years, and during it the vertebrates experienced their greatest radiation. The variety of forms of vertebrate on land, in sea and in the air has probably never been rivalled either before or since. Looked at objectively, this was the high-water mark of vertebrate life on earth. From the point of view of the mammals it was an unmitigated disaster, since it held up their advance for a hundred million years. Had this long period not intervened, the true mammals, and with them, of course, man, might have evolved a hundred million years earlier. If only because they completely dominated the faunas of the Jurassic and Cretaceous, the dinosaurs and their allies must be considered.[36,37,38] These cold-blooded carnivorous and herbivorous reptiles fed by day and, presumably, slept by night. This diurnal habit allowed the tiny warm-blooded mammals of the period to flourish by night and so survive. At the time when the land was dominated by the mammal-like reptiles, the ancestors of the dinosaurs, the early lepidosaurs, such as the millerosaurs, were the main terrestrial invertebrate-feeders. The great archosaur radiation began with small diapsid reptiles, which developed an opening in the side of the skull in front of the orbits; this preorbital fenestra is the hallmark of the archosaurs and, in life, it housed an important gland.

Bipedal *versus* Quadrupedal Ancestry

The early success of this group is generally attributed to their bipedal mode of locomotion. When the archosaurs first achieved prominence at the end of the Triassic, there is no doubt that the carnivorous members of the group were bipedal. The hind limbs were markedly longer and stronger than the fore limbs and the massive tail acted as an effective counter-weight to the body. Bipedalism was thought to have evolved from the capacity of their lightly built ancestral forms to run on their hind limbs for short distances in emergency, as some lizards do at the present time. The advantage of such bipedalism is that the stride is lengthened and a greater speed achieved. However, the earliest archosaurs, as has been pointed out by C. C. Young,[251] do not fit this picture, for they were all squat animals which clearly spent most of their lives in water (Fig. 35b). It seems evident that the archosaurs at no time, during the radiation of the paramammals, provided any direct competition with them but, instead, established themselves in the ecological niche left vacant by the amphibians. The disparity in size of the limbs and the strong muscular tail, as Charig[33] has argued, can be best explained as adaptations for swimming rather than for bipedalism. In fact, in their general proportions the earliest archosaurs had much in common with living crocodiles, which have been generally considered to be survivors of bipedal ancestors secondarily reverted to a quadrupedal gait. The longer hind limbs and thick muscular tail were regarded as evidence for this, as is the capacity of crocodiles to walk, like mammals, with their legs straight. However, it is possible to interpret the form of the crocodile in a quite different manner. As Charig[33] has stressed, 'Could it not be that the earliest archosaurs were amphibious—like the mesosaurs and otters—using their tail for propulsion in the water and their hind limbs for paddling, steering or pushing on the bottom? The greater importance of the hind limb in aquatic locomotion is shown by the increased limb disparity in marine crocodiles and by the fact that in modern crocodiles it is only the hind foot that is webbed.' The ability to walk, as opposed to sprawling, can be explained simply as a development to hold the limbs in the vertical plane and so give a more efficient and rapid gait. This was exactly what happened in the paramammals, and there has never been any suggestion that it was due to any ancestral bipedalism. It seems clear that the massive muscular tail and the strongly developed hind limbs were adaptations to an aquatic mode of life. This also makes it easier to understand how the archosaurs were able to develop these particular traits without coming into competition with the ruling reptiles of the day, the paramammals. At the same time, it explains why the ascendancy of the archosaurs was such a sudden and violent affair. The better adapted the archosaurs became for an aquatic existence, the more preadapted they became for bipedalism. So, when they ventured onto land, the easiest mode of progression would have been on their hind limbs with the tail held out as a counter-balance. They would then have been able to take prodigious strides compared with those of any quadruped, and, being active carnivores, they would have played havoc with the normal faunas. Although the radiation of the lizards must have been a key factor in the decline of the paramammals, their end was undoubtedly hastened by the advent of these archosaurian bounders. At the close of the Triassic a considerable range of archosaurs was established. Among the semiaquatic forms, armoured stagonolepids were herbivores, as Walker[235] has shown. Of the carnivorous types, one of the most successful were the phytosaurs, which seem to have occupied the exact ecological niche of modern crocodiles. The only important difference was in the position of the nostrils, which were situated in front of the eyes. This feature is commonly found in air-breathing aquatic vertebrates, since it allows the air passage to bypass the greater part of the oral cavity. With the mouth open or with food in it, it is still possible for air to pass to the lungs. The crocodiles have accomplished the same end result by developing a secondary palate which has, in fact, a greater posterior extent than that of any mammal; an homologous structure performs an identical function, but for entirely different reasons.

Dinosaurs

During the latter part of the Triassic period the dinosaurs made their appearance. These reptiles belong to two different archosaurian stocks, distinguished by the character of their pelvic girdles; those with the normal reptilian triradiate girdle are the Saurischia (Fig. 35a), those with the quadriradiate, as in the birds, are the Ornithischia (Fig. 36ai). The earliest ornithischian is known only from a skull, remarkable for its heterodont pseudo-mammalian dentition (Fig. 36aii). The saurischians, on the other hand, were represented by two groups, the heavy quadrupedal sauropods which were clearly plant-eaters, and the carnivorous bipedal theropods. This latter group consisted of the dominant carnivores during the remainder of the Mesozoic. Incidentally, it was the distal end of the femur of a carnivorous dinosaur that was the earliest fossil reptile ever to be described (Plot 1677),[163] subsequently in 1763 named by Brookes[26] *Scrotum humanum*!

Since restorations of the giant theropods, such as *Tyrannosaurus*, are so familiar, it would seem appropriate to give some account of Newman's[131] radically different interpretation of their structure and also his conclusions as to their gait. It is clear that these animals could only have walked on their hind limbs; the fore limbs were reduced to vestiges, although the pectoral musculature must have been substantial. Newman[132] has postulated that the fore limbs played an important role in assisting the animal to rise from a resting position, by preventing the extension of the hind limbs from simply pushing the animal forward along the ground. In considering the stance of *Tyrannosaurus*, Newman[131] notes that in the only well preserved vertebral column the dorsal region was rigid, with a mobile neck set

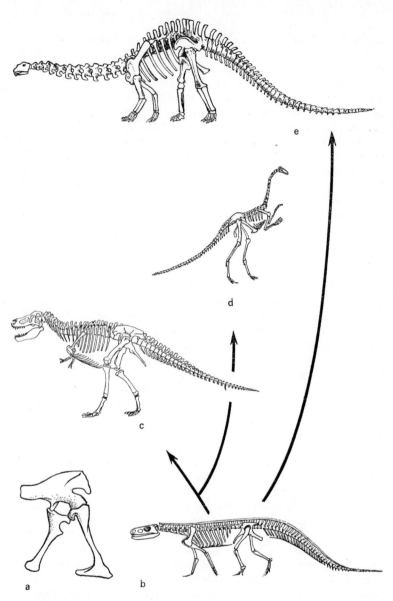

FIG. 35. a. Saurischian pelvis viewed from right side; b. *Ticinosuchus* (Middle Triassic); c. *Tyrannosaurus* (Cretaceous), from Newman; d. *Ornithomimus* (Cretaceous); e. *Apatosaurus* (Jurassic). (after Krebs, Newman and Maleev).

off at a marked angle. The tail, which must have acted as a counter-balance, was probably rigid in its distal part and, like the dorsal region of the vertebral column, would have been held in a horizontal position. From the evidence available Newman insists that the tail should be shortened by some twelve feet. If the vertebral column were orientated at 45°, as it was in all other restorations, then the tail, even with twelve feet amputated, would have dragged on the ground. From the evidence of footprints, it is certain that the tail was habitually held free of the ground. In birds, which do not have a bony tail to act as a counter-balance, the femur is held rigidly in a horizontal plane and the stride is from the knee joint. In such bipedal animals it is necessary to retain the centre of gravity over each leg in turn when the animal walks, and this is accomplished by alternately bringing the legs under the body, the toes pointing inwards. The result is a waddling gait producing a sinuous trackway. Although the carnivorous dinosaurs were not so well adapted as the birds, nevertheless the fossil trackways show them to have had a comparable gait. The femur was longer than the tibia, in contrast to the avian arrangement, and so must have been involved in walking. It must have been held forward although not in a horizontal plane, but it could only have moved through a small arc, as is evidenced from the short stride. From the structure of the acetabulum, it is clear that the femur could not have moved back to a vertical position (Fig. 35c). In spite of approaching the avian situation, the tail was still required to act as an effective counter-balance. Newman's interpretation of theropod stance and gait is consistent with the principles that apply to the large running birds.

The herbivorous group of saurischians, the sauropods, include such huge forms as the famous *Brontosaurus* and *Diplodocus* (Fig. 35e). The huge skeletons of these animals have provoked the suggestion that they had to spend most of their lives propped up by water, the bones being unable to support the body weight in air. Certainly they were amphibious, spending much of their time in swamps and estuaries, feeding on the abundant soft vegetation. Again, their nostrils were situated just in front of their eyes, a strong indication of an aquatic mode of life. The hind limbs were generally longer than the fore limbs, but this is no longer a valid reason for suggesting that they had secondarily reverted to a quadrupedal posture. It is now quite evident that this group had simply remained quadrupedal. One group, to which *Brachiosaurus* belongs, had a very marked limb disparity, but in this case the fore limbs were longer than the hind. This genus is generally restored with its neck raised giving the animal a height of over forty feet. Since *Brachiosaurus* was amphibious, it was thought that it was able to walk on the bottom of lakes and rivers with its nostrils above the water surface. This pleasing concept has been demolished by Kermack,[101] who calculated that the pressure on the animal's lungs at such depths would preclude the possibility of breathing. *Brachiosaurus* should be reconstructed with its neck held more or less horizontally, like all its relatives, rather than in a dramatic vertical pose. These animals were sensational enough as it was, without needing any postural embellishments.

The remaining group of dinosaurs, the ornithischians, were exclusively plant-eaters—the earliest complete skeletons known come from the beginning of the Jurassic period and are of fairly squat, heavily armoured, quadrupedal animals. Again, there was a strong muscular tail and a marked disparity in the lengths of the limbs. The main difference between these forms and their ancestors was the development of the bony scutes into a veritable armour, which Colbert[36] called the 'hands-off trend'. These primitive armoured dinosaurs gave rise to the stegosaurs, with their double row of triangular plates along the ridge of the back and several pairs of sharp spines on the tail (Fig. 36a, b). For all their fearsome appearance, these animals were quite defenceless except for the tail. The great dorsal plates would have offered no protection whatsoever, being probably just for display. *Stegosaurus* is the reptile popularly considered to have had a 'second brain', or at least a sacral ganglion larger than the brain. There is a frequently quoted poem on the subject; my only reason for not quoting it here is that the 'sacral ganglion', as H. M. Smith[13] pointed out, was in all probability the glycogen gland, comparable with that of birds. It was such an attractive idea and it has become so entrenched in dinosaur lore that its demise is a cause for some regret.

The other armoured group, the ankylosaurs, were more successful than the stegosaurs. They became exceedingly squat, ground-hugging animals, with a very solid covering of thick bony plates and frequently with bony club-like tails (Fig. 36c).

The ornithopods were the most successful of the ornithischians and at first glance looked remarkably like the bipedal theropods. Their ridged teeth, however, were clearly developed for a herbivorous diet. Their footprints show that they were often bipedal and that they too held the tail free of the ground, but their fore limbs were never drastically reduced. Indeed they bore hooves, suggesting that the normal gait was quadrupedal; only in emergencies, or when they wanted to feed off higher branches of the trees, would they have run on their hind limbs or taken up a bipedal stance. These animals can be considered as facultative bipeds. Some of the smaller forms seem to have been capable of climbing trees, and it may well be that such animals gave rise to the birds.

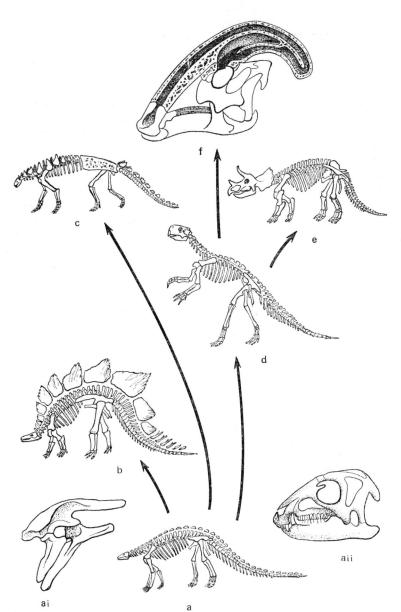

FIG. 36. ai. Ornithischian pelvis viewed from right side. aii. *Heterodonto-saurus* (Triassic); a. *Scelidosaurus* (Lower Jurassic); *Stegosaurus* (Upper Jurassic); c. *Polacanthus* (Lower Cretaceous); d. *Psittacosaurus* (Lower Cretaceous); e. *Triceratops* (Upper Cretaceous); f. *Parasaurolophus*, hadrosaur showing extent of nasal passage (Upper Cretaceous). (after Crompton and Charig, Ostrom, Rozdestivenski and Maleev).

Towards the end of the Cretaceous period one group of ornithopods, the hadrosaurs or duck-billed dinosaurs, were remarkably successful (Fig. 36f). They developed on their skulls weird tubular outgrowths which were, in fact, formed by the nasal bones. The nasal passages passed up these tubes and then doubled back to enter the pharynx. These structures were thought to have housed accessory air supplies, so that the animals could stay under water. Certain hadrosaurs probably spent their lives in a watery environment, but no-one has satisfactorily explained how such an apparatus could have functioned. Recently Ostrom[154] has provided an alternative theory suggesting that the increased area of the nasal passages augmented the sensitivity of the olfactory organs. He noted that the hadrosaurs appeared to be by far the most vulnerable of all the dinosaurs, and yet they evidently flourished. With a significant improvement of the sense of smell they would have had forewarning of the approach of their predators.

Another feature much remarked upon is the hadrosaur dentition, in which there were as many as 2,000 teeth in the jaws at any one time. The teeth were small and closely packed in rows, being continuously replaced from below so that during life there was a permanent, wide, ridged occlusal surface. The ridges were produced by the differential wear of the dentine and enamel. This type of homodont dentition was developed to enable these animals to deal effectively with much tougher plant material; for the end of the Cretaceous marked the spread of the angiosperms, and hence the establishment of the modern flora. The plants were more siliceous and required grinding for their nutritive value to be extracted, and the hadrosaur dentition accomplished this feat. In view of this the extinction of the hadrosaurs is a matter for surprise.

Contemporary with the hadrosaurs and equally successful, so it seemed, were a further group of ornithischians, the ceratopsians (Fig. 36e). These animals were unarmoured quadrupeds; but they developed, at the back of their skulls, large bony frills with long projections covering and protecting the vulnerable part of the neck. There were also bony 'horns' on the snout. The protection afforded by these outgrowths was quite different from that provided by the development of the original bony scutes. The evolution of this group late in the Mesozoic indicates that it was not, like the other quadrupedal groups, directly derived from semiaquatic ancestors. Fortunately there are facultatively bipedal ornithopods from the Cretaceous of Mongolia which in their skulls show the incipient development of the beaked snout and bony frill of the ceratopsians (Fig. 36d). Here, at long last, is one group of dinosaurs representing a secondary reversion to a quadrupedal gait from a bipedal, albeit facultative.

The dinosaurs, after dominating life on the land for a hundred million years, then disappeared; after a decline lasting several million years before the close of the Cretaceous, their final disappearance was, however, a sudden event, and moreover one that has never been satisfactorily explained. The end of the dinosaurs had an important consequence, for it left the field clear for the resurgence of the theropsids, which had by this time become true mammals.

12 : Return to the Sea

During the age of dinosaurs the reptiles also dominated life in the sea. By contrast with the situation on land, the reptilian population of the seas included few archosaurs and lepidosaurs. The main reptilian invasion of the seas took place in the Triassic, when the ray-finned fish deserted the freshwaters of the rivers for salt water. The reptiles, therefore, followed their food, the fish. At this time the paramammals were entirely occupied with the conquest of the land, having, as it were, turned their backs on the water.

Ichthyosaurs

The ichthyosaurs were apparently the most perfectly adapted of the marine reptiles. They were fish-like in their general shape, and swam by means of a powerful tail with a striking dorsal fin (Fig. 37b). The limbs of the ichthyosaurs were paddles with increased numbers both of phalanges and of digits. They had no legs as such; indeed there is no evidence that the ichthyosaurs evolved from any other group of reptiles. In fact, they must be derived directly from amphibians. Moreover, there is no evidence that this group originated from any terrestrial ancestor. What little evidence we have, suggests that they simply became better adapted to an aquatic existence than their contemporary amphibian relatives. The pattern of skull roofing bones at the back of the skull is certainly more reminiscent of the amphibians than of the reptiles—indeed some authors actually prefer to classify them as amphibians.[5] There is, however, some information available on their mode of reproduction. As these animals could not have ventured onto land, they could not have laid shelled eggs. Many specimens have been found proving that the ichthyosaurs gave birth to live young. Embryos have been discovered within the mother, some even on the point of emerging (Fig. 37a). The difficulty is in deciding whether the young developed from an amniote egg; in other words

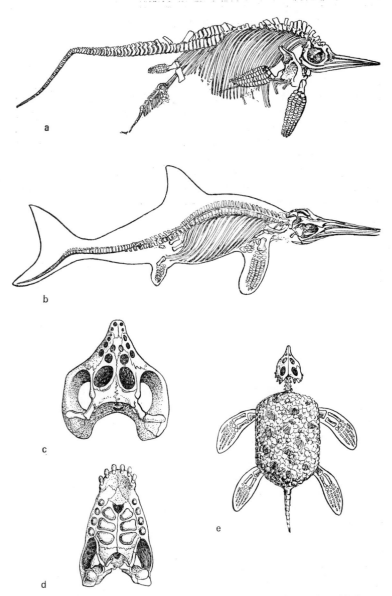

FIG. 37. a. Ichthyosaur killed and preserved at moment of giving birth;
b. ichthyosaur with skin impression showing body outline; c–e. placodonts: c. *Cyamodus*, palatal view (Middle Triassic); d. *Placodus*, palatal
view (Middle Triassic); e. *Placochelys*, restoration in dorsal view (Upper
Triassic).

were the ichthyosaurs true reptiles and oviviviparous, or were they viviparous and therefore by definition not reptiles? Frankly, there is no real way of telling, but it seems far the more likely that the ichthyosaurs had evolved an alternative to the amniote egg in which the early development took place within the mother, making them totally independent of the land. This alone does not, however, justify their exclusion from the reptiles, as they do possess a majority of skeletal features assigning them to a higher structural grade than that of the Amphibia. In any case their non-possession of the amniote egg is non-proven.

Judging from their numerous fine sharply pointed teeth, the early ichthyosaurs seem to have been fish-eaters; some however had the characteristic rounded teeth of shellfish-eaters.

Placodonts

The placodonts, known only from the Triassic, were exclusively mollusc-eaters, and had developed great crushing plates as well as incisor-like teeth for pulling up shellfish, presumably the stalks of brachiopods (Fig. 37c–e). The success of shellfish-eating reptiles during the Trias is in all likelihood due to the earlier extinction of the mollusc-eating cartilaginous fish in Permo-Carboniferous times. The extinction of these reptiles at the end of the Trias was in all probability due to the evolution of the modern rays and skates and the ray-finned fish of the Jurassic. The demise of these marine reptiles may well have been due to their inability to compete with the fish, whose respiratory mechanism did not require frequent trips to the surface. In any direct competition for bottom-living food, the fish would have the advantage.

Nothosaurs

Shore-dwelling fish-feeders, the nothosaurs, made their appearance in the Trias. Unlike the ichthyosaurs', the nothosaurs' limbs retained all the elements of the terrestrial type, although beginning to develop into paddles. The hands and feet were webbed and, in addition, the form of the neural spines of the tail vertebrae indicate the presence of a dorsal tail fin (Fig. 38). There is no doubt that the nothosaurs were really derived from fully terrestrial ancestors, but there is doubt as to whether these ancestors possessed the amniote egg. Unlike the ichthyosaurs, the nothosaurs were capable of travelling on land, so that laying an egg on the shore would have presented no difficulties. There is some evidence that the nothosaurs gave birth to live young. Kuhn-Schnyder[114] has recently published a photograph (reproduced

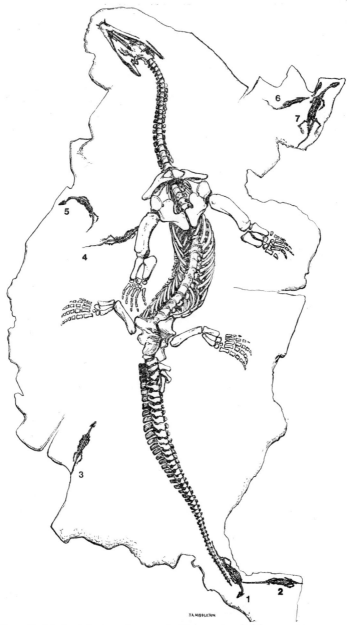

FIG. 38. Adult nothosaur, in ventral view, surrounded by seven young (Middle Triassic).

here, as a drawing, in Fig. 38) showing a specimen of an adult nothosaur surrounded by seven young. The most reasonable explanation of this occurrence is that they were indeed the young of the adult in question and that the mother died shortly after giving birth.[225] This interpretation is disputed by Kuhn-Schnyder (personal communication) who claims that the small individuals were preyed upon by the larger, and that in any case the large and small belong to different genera. The fact that young nothosaurs commonly ended up in the droppings of adults should occasion no surprise; the greatest hazard for young crocodiles is the appetite of their parents! The proportions of the different parts of the skeleton are different in the young and the adult, and therefore this classification of young and adult into separate genera may be suspect. If, however, it is accepted that the nothosaurs gave birth to live young, exactly the same problem as in the ichthyosaurs immediately arises. It seems reasonable to suggest a comparable solution.[225] This interpretation would seem to be reinforced if the descendants of the nothosaurs, the plesiosaurs, are taken into consideration. The later members of the latter group must have been incapable of getting onto land to lay eggs; so by this stage of their evolution the plesiosaurs must have been able to give birth to live young. In view of this, it seems more than likely that their success as ocean-going reptiles was a consequence of this capacity.

Plesiosaurs

The plesiosaurs evolved from the nothosaurs during the Triassic, and during the succeeding Jurassic and Cretaceous periods they showed a gradual improvement in their overall structure. To all intents and purposes, they inhabited an unchanging environment, and their evolution shows a steady progression as the animals became better adapted for their particular mode of life. Unlike most other marine reptiles, the plesiosaurs swam by means of their large paddles; their tails were comparatively small, although the presence of a dorsal fin indicates that they must have played some role in locomotion, perhaps as a steering device.[211,133]

Two distinct lineages evolved from the predominantly fish-eating forms of the Trias, differing primarily in their dietary preferences. One group, culminating in the elasmosaurs, became better adapted for fish-eating, the other, the pliosaurs, took to eating cephalopods (Fig. 39). The fish-eating forms retained large numbers of simple sharply pointed slender teeth, with the upper and lower dentitions acting together as a fish trap. These reptiles showed a gradual elongation of the fore paddles, the propodials (humeri and femora) were shortened, and the pectoral girdle became flattened and greatly extended in front of the shoulder joint (Fig. 39b). Watson[237] has analysed this sequence of changes in the character of the limbs and their girdles. The shortening of the propodials meant that the main musculature of the limbs was also shortened. The mechanical advantage became poorer and the animal could not have made powerful swimming strokes, but it could

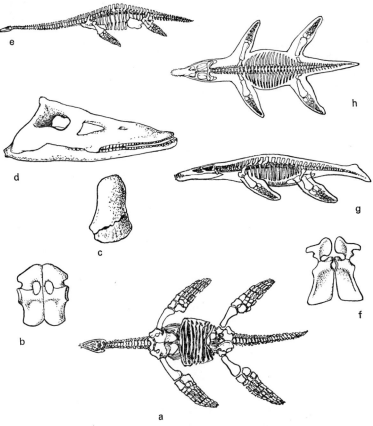

FIG. 39. Plesiosaurs

a. *Rhomaleosaurus*, ventral view (Lower Jurassic); b. pectoral girdle of elasmosaur showing anterior development of scapulae; c. short propodial of cimoliasaur; d. skull of *Aristonectes*, a cimoliasaur (Upper Cretaceous); e. *Muraenosaurus* (Upper Jurassic); f. pectoral girdle of pliosaur; g, h. pliosaur *Liopleurodon* in lateral and dorsal views (Upper Jurassic). (after Novozhilov, Persson, Newman and Halstead Tarlo).

K

have produced rapid flicks of the paddles. This type of limb was specialised for speed, not for power. The flattening of the girdle ensured that the vertical play of the fore limb was reduced to a minimum, restricting its plane of movement to the horizontal and so precluding an effective diving action. The anterior production of the pectoral girdle meant that the limb musculature concerned with drawing the limbs forwards became as important as that pulling them back, so making the backing stroke as effective as the forward swimming stroke. The sum total of these modifications resulted in a highly manoeuvrable animal capable of twisting and turning with great speed. This agility, however, was restricted to the surface waters of the sea. Coupled with these changes, the head became progressively smaller and the neck longer. In some of the late Cretaceous genera there were up to seventy vertebrae in the neck. Indeed these animals fitted Conybeare's classic description of 'a serpent threaded through a turtle'. Although almost entirely submerged beneath the surface of the sea (apart from their nostrils), the exaggerated necks of these animals would have made it physically impossible for them to twist and turn their bodies with speed if their necks remained submerged. The arc described by the neck and head with the animal turning through 180° or even a mere 90° would have been prodigious and certainly could not have been accomplished speedily against the frictional resistance of the water. The inevitable conclusion is that the head and the greater part of the neck were lifted out of the water during rapid manoeuvring, swinging over the surface and dropping in again on the sighting of fish. This high degree of manoeuvrability not only enabled the long-necked plesiosaurs to fish efficiently but also must have been equally advantageous in helping them to escape the attentions of predators.

The short-necked forms, the pliosaurs, were in marked contrast to the long-necked plesiosaurs. In the pliosaurs the teeth became more massive, blunter and not so closely packed in the jaw, whilst the skull became progressively larger and the neck concomitantly shorter (Fig. 39g, h). As Newman and I[133] have shown, the skulls of these animals became proportionally larger in relation to the rest of the body as each animal developed. These animals were specialised for feeding on squid and cuttle-fish; myriads of chitinous hooks from cephalopod tentacles are commonly found in their stomachs. The large jaws and massive teeth were ideally suited for trapping and killing cephalopods. The pectoral girdle did not become flat but retained important dorsal components, so allowing the front paddles to be raised above the horizontal plane, thus enabling the animal to dive through the water after its prey and not restricting it to surface waters.[211] There was no further development of the girdle in front of the glenoid; therefore, the important backing stroke of the long-necked forms was not possible in the pliosaurs. The propodial bones remained long, giving a good mechanical advantage and consequently a powerful swimming stroke. The pliosaurs must have been powerful swimmers well adapted to hunting down cephalopods, although they did not have the agility of their surface paddling small-headed relatives.

In the general proportions of the skeleton, feeding behaviour and locomotion the plesiosaurs fall into two basic groups. Persson[159,160] has, however, described a group of Cretaceous plesiosaurs with large heads and short necks that do not fit this pattern, since at the same time they had short propodials and numerous fine sharp teeth (Fig. 39c, d). Some authors have suggested that these forms were pliosaurs, but Persson assigned them to the long-necked group on account of the specialisation of their limbs. This approach is clearly the more correct, since it is obvious that these animals fed on a diet of fish and were adapted for swimming at the surface of the sea in exactly the same way as the long-necked forms and not at all like the pliosaurs. As far as their habits were concerned, there is no doubt as to their affinities.

The pliosaurs were the important cephalopod-feeders during the Jurassic and Cretaceous periods, but the ichthyosaurs also took to a similar diet, as is shown by their stubbier teeth and also by the nature of their stomach contents.[164] The ichthyosaurs give the impression of having been the best adapted of all the marine reptiles; but they seem to have gone into something of a decline during the early part of the Cretaceous. During the Jurassic, when the ichthyosaurs reached their acme, the crocodiles returned to the sea. They became fully marine, evolving paddle-like limbs and dorsal tail fins; and their teeth demonstrate that they were, in the main, fish-eaters. During the early part of the Cretaceous, some of them seem to have become cephalopod-eaters, following the pattern of the ichthyosaurs and plesiosaurs, starting off with fish and only later developing a taste for cuttlefish!

Mosasaurs

The last important group of reptiles to colonise the sea were a side-branch of the varanid lizards, the mosasaurs. These animals were veritable sea serpents. Their bodies were greatly attenuated with a long deep tail and flipper-like limbs. The teeth were similar to those of the pliosaurs, leading to the inference that like them they were cephalopod-eaters. A large ammonite has been described showing a sequence of fifteen mosasaur bites—further evidence as to the diet of these animals.[99] Towards the very end of the Cretaceous, presumably in response to the decline of many of the cephalopod groups that took place at that time, some of the mosasaurs became shellfish-eaters and their teeth developed into hemispherical knobs—ideal for crushing lamellibranchs which had ecologically replaced the brachipods as the main sedentary shellfish of the sea bed.

Evolution of Marine Food Chains

At the end of the Cretaceous period all these marine reptiles became extinct. However, the significance of the variety of marine reptiles during the Mesozoic is that they saw the establishment of the modern food chain cycle in the seas. In the Palaeozoic era the dominant life in the seas were the cephalopods; the only important marine vertebrates were the sharks and their relatives, which were mainly shellfish-eaters. The food-chain pyramid had the phytoplankton at its base, then the zooplankton, thereafter the arthropods and finally, at the top, the cephalopods. In the Triassic the bony fish invaded the seas and must have rapidly rivalled the cephalopods for the position at the peak of the pyramid. During this period the reptiles too entered the sea, although in the main remaining shore-based. The ichthyosaurs, askeptosaurs and nothosaurs were all fish-eaters, and so occupied the summit of the pyramid. At this same time the reptiles filled the ecological niche left vacant by the sharks and the placodonts, and some ichthyosaurs became shellfish-eaters. At the beginning of the Jurassic the sharks re-emerged as mollusc-eaters, and the bony fish too competed for the same niche, resulting in the simultaneous elimination of the mollusc-eating reptiles.

Coincident with this change some vertebrates, the ichthyosaurs and pliosaurs, began to feed on cephalopods, although still retaining a partially fishy diet at this stage. For the remainder of the Mesozoic, there was a more clear cut dietary division among the marine reptiles. In the Jurassic, there were the fish-eating long-necked plesiosurs and marine crocodiles and the cephalopod-eating pliosaurs and ichthyosaurs. The two groups of plesiosaur survived into the Cretaceous, as did some of the crocodiles which began to feed on cephalopods; but the ichthyosaurs declined. The end of the Mesozoic heralded the mosasaurs, which were mainly cephalopod-eaters, although one small group adapted to a diet of shellfish right at the very end just prior to the extinction of all the marine reptiles. Towards the end of the Mesozoic the most successful of the marine reptiles seem to have been cephalopod-feeders. The reason for this was, in all probability, the evolution of the modern bony fish, the teleosts. The main lines of the modern teleost faunas were already established by the end of the Cretaceous, and it is more than likely that the reptiles that had been able to hunt the more heavily armoured, and consequently slower, holostean bony fish were unable to catch enough of their more agile and speedy descendants to ensure their survival. Hence the predominance of cephalopod-eaters. A break in the food chain—the mass extinction of the cephalopods—is likely to have been the cause of the elimination of these reptiles.

No land vertebrates seem to have ventured back to the sea until the Lower Eocene.[4,100] It is interesting to note that the proportions of the early whales were similar to those of the mosasaurs; they were elongated 'sea serpents' in fact. Their teeth indicate a diet of cephalopods. The success of the whales may be correlated with the minor evolutionary radiation of the nautiloid cephalopods in the Eocene. By the turn of the Oligocene, the modern toothed whales or odontocetes were in evidence. These were much shorter, streamlined animals perfectly capable of hunting down the fastest teleosts. The speed of modern cetaceans such as the dolphin is now known to be due to the remarkable properties of their skin which permits laminar flow over the body, thus to all intents and purposes eliminating the friction of the water. The modern dolphin has numerous sharply pointed teeth and is a fish-eater. The sperm whale has large, stumpy, well-separated teeth and is a cephalopod-feeder; the beaked dolphin is toothless, since the modern cephalopods have few hard parts and teeth are not so vital; it manages perfectly adequately, spitting out the cuttle-fish bone before swallowing its prey.[192] Another group of mammals that have taken to the sea and in the main are fish-eaters are the seals. A notable exception is the so-called crab-eating seal, which, in fact, filters crustaceans from the water, its teeth acting as a kind of sieve. The walrus, a relative of the seals, is a shellfish-eater, and its teeth are correspondingly rounded and peg-like. These animals have exaggerated their canines into tusks which serve to root up shells.

The aquatic mammals, the cetaceans and pinnipeds, clearly re-occupied the ecological niches left vacant by the extinction of the marine reptiles. At the same time they fitted into comparable positions in the food chain pyramid. However the penultimate part of the summit was taken by mammals that preyed upon the fish and cephalopod-eating mammals. These are animals like the killer whales, which feed on seals and dolphins; Slijper[192] records finding the partially digested remains of thirteen dolphins and fourteen seals in the stomach of one specimen.

During the Tertiary, however, a further group of marine mammals evolved, which did not fit into the normal food chain pattern as the other mammals and the marine reptiles before them. These were the whale-bone whales or mystacetes, which fed directly on the zooplankton and achieved the distinction of being the largest animal to have evolved. There is no doubt that until the advent of man these animals were extremely successful. At first glance it would appear that feeding as close as possible to the base of the food-chain pyramid would have been a retrograde step, but in fact it is the opposite. In the energy-flow from plant material through the various stages up to, say, killer whales, the wastage of protein from stage to stage is vastly increased the nearer the peak of the pyramid is approached. Thus, the nearer to the source of energy, the more efficient and effective the food supply. As far as farming the sea is concerned, the maximum protein return would be obtained from phyto- and zooplankton and certainly not from whales.

Finally, for the sake of completeness, the current peak of the food-chain pyramid must be mentioned. This is man, who preys upon marine mammals for food and clothing in polar regions. At present there seems every likelihood that the larger whales are going to be extinguished by man in the near future. In terms of the general economy of the seas this is not serious, whereas a break in the food chain nearer the base would have disastrous consequences. The great variety and mixed history of air-breathing aquatic vertebrates is a consequence of their position at the top of the food-chain pyramid; for it is here that there is the greatest changeover of personnel.

13 : Conquest of the Air

Not only did the reptiles come to dominate the sea and the land; they also conquered the air. To overcome the effects of gravity, the basic structure of the reptilian body had to undergo a number of changes. What stimulus provoked some reptiles into flight? The insects provide a clue. During the Carboniferous they must have formed the main food supply of the smaller amphibians. Taking to the air is an obvious way of escaping from a water- or land-bound predator, and this the insects did during the Carboniferous with its luxuriant vegetation cover. First of all they would have climbed tree trunks, thereafter jumping from tree to tree; increasing the length of the jump by the development of lateral outgrowths would have led to gliding, itself a prelude to, and an integral part of, flying.

Triassic lizards such as *Icarosaurus* were the first vertebrates to launch themselves into the air (Fig. 34d).[39,172,216] These animals were not true fliers, but parachutists or gliders, characterised by long hollow paper-thin ribs projecting laterally from the vertebral column and capable of being folded back against the body. It is quite clear that like the living 'flying lizard', *Draco*, they had a membrane stretched over the ribs to form a gliding plate. Although undoubtedly these animals were efficient gliders the form of their 'wing' or patagium must have precluded them from evolving into genuine flying vertebrates.

Pterosaurs

In fact, at the end of the Triassic period there appeared the first true flying vertebrates, the pterosaurs. These were archosaurs, but nothing is known of their ancestry in the fossil record. Presumably they evolved a gliding membrane as an escape mechanism, as had the lizards before them. This time, however, it was an extension of skin from the side of the body supported by the fore and hind limbs (Fig. 40a–c). The anterior part of the patagium was fixed to a greatly elongated fourth finger, so that it could be extended laterally as a gliding plane and could also function as a wing.[74] The history of the pterosaurs shows a progressive advance in their adaptation to aerial life. The earliest adequately known forms come from the Lower Jurassic and have heavy skulls with a battery of teeth; they also had long tails. In order to fly, it is essential that the weight of the body should be reduced to a minimum, and this is accomplished by lightening all the bones. When pterosaur bones were first discovered near Cambridge, they were identified as those of geese; which is not surprising, since in fragments bird and pterosaur bones are virtually indistinguishable. Extensions of the lungs filled all the available spaces, including those in the bones. The development of such pneumatic bone seems to have been a feature of both pterosaurs and birds, although first evolved in the pterosaurs. Another method of reducing weight is to dispense with the teeth. These are solid and heavy and, although present in the early forms, were discarded in the advanced pterosaurs. Another place where weight reduction can be expected is in the long bony tail. Any flying animal must be stable in its flight medium, and stability can be achieved in a number of ways. With two laterally placed gliding planes, the tendency to roll from side to side will be overcome. However, there must be some means of overcoming the tendency to pitch. Pitch is prevented by the presence of a long stiff tail projecting posteriorly and so producing a horizontal surface behind the centre of gravity. If the body of the animal starts to pitch forwards it will lift the tail up and this movement has to be made against gravity so the weight of the tail will keep the body on an even keel. The stiff tail therefore acts as an automatic stabiliser. The need to reduce weight obviously conflicts with the vital role of the tail in locomotion. In stable flight, any forces that may disturb the course of the animal will, because of the structures present, automatically be corrected without any effort on the part of the animal. However, this form of stability is not without its problems. The degree of manoeuvrability is severely restricted; it is simply not possible for the animal to turn rapidly, and furthermore, for a given weight the stalling speed must have been comparatively high. The size of the animals would thus have been determined primarily by the speed at which they came in to land and the degree of shock they could withstand on impact. With instability, as Maynard Smith[195] has pointed out, greater manoeuvrability is possible and flying more slowly without stalling, so allowing an increase in size. Instability is achieved by losing the tail, a loss which has the added advantage of further reducing the weight. However, there are no longer any automatic correctors of pitch; so it is possible to change to instable flight only if there are some other means of maintaining balance. The animal has to be quickly aware of

FIG. 40. a–c. *Pterodactylus* (Upper Jurassic): a. sketch of fossil; b. reconstruction of skeleton; c. restoration. d. e. *Archaeopteryx* (Upper Jurassic): d. sketch of fossil; e. reconstruction of skeleton.

its state of balance and has to be able consciously to take the appropriate action for maintaining it, if necessary. With the evolution of a basic instability there is an increase in the parts of the brain concerned with sight, balance and muscular coordination. The brain in the pterosaurs became essentially avian, the skull more rounded and the sutures more tightly knitted.

Among the pterosaurs, there evolved small sparrow-sized forms (Fig. 40a–c), with short broad wings denoting that they were capable of some form of flapping flight, and others, generally the larger forms, with comparatively longer and narrower wings specially adapted for gliding and riding air-currents. The efficiency of these flying reptiles, as ascertained from their skeletal anatomy, means that they must have been capable of sustained flight. This is possible only if the animals concerned are able to maintain a high metabolic rate, and this itself demands a degree of homoiothermy. It follows that the pterosaurs were warm-blooded. This conclusion is supported by some indirect evidence. Some pterosaurs had plumes on their heads; and this, like the whiskers of the paramammals, indicates that both had a hairy, or in the case of the pterosaurs, a 'downy', covering. Such hair or down would have acted as a body insulator.

In any flying machine, the larger it becomes the more power it requires, and the power needed increases at a higher rate than the linear increase in size, if the general proportions remain the same. Since the only source of increased power in flying animals is the musculature, there must be a disproportionate increase in this; which of course increases the weight. There comes a point beyond which the whole system will no longer function. The maximum weight of a flying vertebrate is calculated to be about 50 lbs. Were this not the case, as Haldane noted, 'eagles might be as large as tigers and as formidable to man as hostile aeroplanes'. Haldane calculated that for a man to fly he would need such enormous wing muscles that the keel of the sternum would need to be over 4 ft. long and his legs reduced to spindly stilts! The largest flying vertebrate that ever existed was the ocean-going Cretaceous pterosaur *Pteranodon*, which had a wing span up to 27 ft., and was at the upper limit of size permissible for a living flying object. It has been suggested that pterosaurs such as this cared for their young, since it would not have been possible for the females to have carried eggs commensurate with the size expected. They would have had to lay very small eggs, and when newly-hatched the young would have been quite unable to fend for themselves; *ergo* the parents cared for them.

The pterosaurs were highly successful during the Jurassic and Cretaceous, although their dominance was somewhat blunted by the birds towards the end of the Cretaceous, except for the ocean-going *Pteranodon*. The first birds made their appearance in the latter part of the Jurassic, at a time when the peterosaurs completely dominated life in the air. The success of the birds and their ultimate ousting of the pterosaurs presents an interesting problem, since the first birds were unable to fly and could therefore have been of little consequence in any direct competition with the pterosaurs.

Birds

The first bird was a woodland dweller and is known from only three specimens (Fig. 4od, e). Nevertheless, *Archaeopteryx* is perhaps the most famous of all fossils. It is assigned to the birds because it had feathers, but, in the majority of its structures, it was entirely reptilian. This animal was not unlike an arboreal ornithopod ornithischian dinosaur; the nature of its bone is reptilian and there is no hint of it being lightened, let alone pneumatic.[207] It has a good battery of teeth and a long reptilian tail, albeit feathered. On the other hand, the foot had one digit pointing backwards, so allowing the animal to perch like a bird (Fig. 4od, e). The fore limb clearly foreshadowed that of birds, the humerus and radius/ulna are avian, and the reduction of the rest of the bones is comparable to the situation in birds. This animal still retained three claws, which must have been necessary for it to scramble up the trees. The young South American hoatzin also has such claws. The 'wing' had nine primary and fourteen secondary feathers, a pattern identical to that of all modern birds. *Archaeopteryx* was a parachutist or glider, and must have launched itself from trees and plunged rapidly to the ground or onto another tree. In no sense could this animal ever have flown. However, even as a gliding animal it had two fundamental advantages over the pterosaurs, and these eventually resulted in the supremacy of the birds over the flying reptiles. One key feature was the separation of the gliding membrane from the hind limb. In most gliding or parachuting vertebrates, the increase in the body surface is produced by an extension of skin outwards from the sides of the body. This skin is stretched out during flight by the fore and hind limbs to which it is attached. This gives a maximal gliding surface which is frequently further expanded by the elongation of parts of the fore limb, as in the pterosaurs and the bats. For flying animals this is perfectly adequate, but, unlike Lack's fictitious swifts, they are obliged to land. With the flying organ attached to the hind limbs, progress on the ground is both slow and clumsy. *Archaeopteryx* had its gliding organ restricted to the fore limb, so that once on the ground it could run with ease. Its gait must have been exactly as that described by Newman for the bipedal dinosaurs, except that the fore limbs would have been tucked in to the side of the body.

The other key advantage was the possession of feathers. A gliding organ formed of feathers was less vulnerable than a thin membrane of skin. Tearing a thin sheet of skin almost inevitably resulted in the death of the animal, for it would be permanently grounded and would have fallen victim to the first predator that happened to come along. In contrast, feathers would simply part, and if any were lost adjacent ones could close the gap; even if this were not sufficient, further growth would replace the lost feathers. Since *Archaeopteryx* could not fly, the possession of feathers could not have been originally for such activity. It seems likely, therefore, that they developed to provide a means of insulating the body. This implies that this group was becoming homoiothermic.

The brain of *Archaeopteryx* shows that it was fully reptilian in its gliding and behaviour, but the subsequent evolution of the birds exactly parallels the pterosaurs in many features. The bone became pneumatic, the teeth were lost, and so was the bony tail which must have acted as an automatic stabiliser. With the development of instability there was a corresponding increase in the power of sight, balance and muscular coordination. These changes are reflected in the structure of the brain, with the enlargement of the cerebral hemispheres, cerebellum, and optic lobes. The skull became swollen and the sutures hardly visible, the bones becoming so firmly united.

With the evolution of the feathered wing, which could be neatly tucked away once the animal was on the ground, and with the bipedal gait, the posture having been somewhat modified as a consequence of the loss of the tail as a counter-balance, the birds were able to be agile on the ground. They must have been effective competitors to the pterosaurs, whose ecological niches they must have rapidly occupied after displacing their original inhabitants. This much is evident with the late Cretaceous birds, but it is necessary to explain the impetus behind the early evolution of the birds, since they were not at first any match for the pterosaurs.

Although incapable of flying, *Archaeopteryx* occupied an ecological niche denied to the majority of pterosaurs. Any densely wooded area, particularly in the Cretaceous when the modern angiosperm flora became established, would have been avoided by the pterosaurs, the birds being left to evolve without competition. Having once achieved modern avian status, the birds were able to invade cliffs on the coast and much more open country, formerly the preserve solely of the pterosaurs.

Perhaps the best known Cretaceous birds are *Hesperornis* and

Ichthyornis. The former genus retained teeth and had reduced its wings to the merest vestiges, having become secondarily flightless. *Ichthyornis,* however, was an excellent flier, although it was reputed to have had teeth. It is now known that the tooth-bearing jaw associated with the skeleton of *Ichthyornis* is that of a baby mosasaur that was fortuitiously preserved with it![207]

Although only a handful of genera are known from the Cretaceous, Fisher[61] has noted that several of the major lines of the radiation of modern birds were already in evidence, even such specialised types as the algal-sifting flamingoes. From that time to the Pleistocene the birds rapidly evolved and spread far and wide, to become one of the most successful vertebrate groups. During the early part of the Tertiary, large, flightless running birds were major carnivores and must have been for a time a serious menace to the mammals of those days. According to Fisher[61] the avifaunas of the Pleistocene marked the high-water mark of bird evolution, and the decrease since then is entirely attributable to the activities of mankind. The most familiar extinctions are those of flightless birds in historic times, the extinct neospecies of the ornithologists, *Aepyornis,* the Roc of Sinbad, the Moa of New Zealand, the Dodo and Solitary of Mauritius, the Great Auk of the North Atlantic finally slaughtered in 1844, the once prolific flying passenger pigeon of North America; and now there is the current deliberate extermination of sea-birds on oceanic islands to make them safe for military aircraft.

14 : Extinction

Perhaps the most dramatic event in the fossil record was the sudden extinction of all the ruling reptiles at the end of the Mesozoic era. The Triassic too was notable for the extinction of numerous groups, but in this instance it is possible to trace gradual ecological replacements, in marked contrast to the situation at the end of the Cretaceous. It is not too difficult to suggest reasons for the extinction of the dinosaurs. The origin and spread of the modern angiosperm flora must have had a profound effect upon animals accustomed to feeding on rather soft plant material. The hadrosaurs seemingly overcame this problem adequately; so it is difficult to account for their demise. The superior brain power of the evolving mammals is sometimes considered to have been a contributory factor, but the intelligence of small nocturnal or crepuscular mammals, such as the hedgehogs and shrews, is unlikely to have weighed greatly in the balance.

The theories that have been propounded are legion, and one cannot do better than quote Jepsen[98] on this topic: 'Authors, with varying competence, have suggested that the dinosaurs disappeared because the climate deteriorated (became suddenly or slowly too hot or cold or dry or wet), or that the diet did (with too much food or not enough of such substances as fern oil; from poisons in water or plants or ingested minerals; the bankruptcy of calcium or other necessary elements). Other writers have put the blame on disease, parasites, wars, anatomical or metabolic disorders (slipped vertebral discs, malfunction or imbalance of hormone or endocrine systems, dwindling brain and consequent stupidity, heat sterilisation), racial old age, evolutionary drift into senescent over-specialisation, changes in the pressure or composition of the atmosphere, poison gases, volcanic dust, excessive oxygen from plants, meteorites, comets, gene pool drainage by little mammalian egg-eaters, overkill capacity by predators, fluctuation of gravitational constants, development of psychotic suicidal factors, entropy, cosmic radiation, shift of Earth's rotational poles, floods, extraction of the moon from the Pacific Basin, drainage of swamp and lake environments, sunspots, God's will, mountain building, raids by little green hunters in flying saucers, lack of even standing room in Noah's Ark, and palaeoweltschmerz'.

The above catalogue includes most of the theories that have been put forward, and one can choose any one or combination of any selected number according to taste. A theory that is intellectually satisfying, will not be viable, if it cannot at the same time explain the simultaneous extinction of both the marine and the flying reptiles. Any theory or combination of theories must be able to adequately explain why these reptiles of land, sea and air all disappeared more or less simultaneously.

Even if the extinctions are satisfactorily explained, one is still faced with the difficulty of the numerous non-extinctions on the one hand and, on the other hand, the question of the groups that had begun important evolutionary radiations during the later part of the Mesozoic and continued them through into the Tertiary with no apparent concern for the great trauma affecting life around them at the Cretaceous-Tertiary boundary. These too must somehow be explained.

In trying to work out the reasons for the great slaughter it should be remembered that the modern angiosperm floras with the modern insect faunas, including the social insects, were already well established. The radiation of the modern lizards was well under way and the snakes had started their radiation. The birds were in the ascendancy and the major lines of their future radiation established. In the seas the modern teleost faunas were flourishing, foreshadowing their present success. The pouched marsupials were in evidence, and so were insectivorous mammals including the deltatheridians which gave rise to the cat-like and hyaena-like creodont carnivores, the condylarths which gave rise to several important groups of ungulate herbivores and also the dog-like creodonts. Last but by no means least the primates, the mammalian order to which man belongs, made its appearance in the Cretaceous. In fact, if one forgets about the dinosaurs and their ilk, it is evident that the late Mesozoic saw the establishment in general outlines of the modern fauna and flora. My own impression is that on land, in the sea and in the air the modern-type faunas were evolving what were basically contemporary food-chain relationships and in this context the giant animals, always the most vulnerable from the point of changing conditions, became irrelevant. In the main the extinct reptilian groups were exceedingly well adapted to particular modes of life but they were not adaptable. This view receives a little support from the two reptilian groups that survived and which one would not have imagined would do so. These are the amphibious crocodiles, which continued virtually unchanged from the Triassic, although the gigantic Cretaceous forms died out, and the chelonians, the turtles and tortoises, also plodding on from the Triassic period when they made their first appearance. These two archaic groups managed by virtue, one suspects, of their primitiveness and adaptability to survive. This accomplishment is only now being seriously affected by man, who at the present rate should extinguish the surviving archosaurs in the not too distant future and make severe inroads into the chelonians.

The penultimate word on the subject of extinction I shall leave to Professor J. Maynard Smith. His poem concerns the small bipedal dinosaur *Struthiomimus*, a late development of the carnivorous dinosaurs with long fingers, by which some believe it could steal the eggs of fellow dinosaurs (cf. Fig. 35d). This contribution to dinosaur lore and literature was written for Professor J. B. S. Haldane on the occasion of his sixtieth birthday and in the original version the penultimate line read 'Remember Prof'. The present version is printed because the moral would seem to have general application.

STRUTHIOMIMUS

or

THE DANGER OF BEING TOO CLEVER

by J. Maynard Smith

The *Dinosaurs*, or so we're told,
Were far too imbecile to hold
Their own against mammalian brains;
Today not one of them remains.
There is another school of thought,
Which says they suffered from a sort
Of constipation from the loss
Of adequate supplies of moss.

But Science now can put before us
The reason true why *Brontosaurus*
Became extinct. In the Cretaceous
A beast incredibly sagacious
Lived and loved and ate its fill;
Long were its legs, and sharp its bill,
Cunning its hands, to steal the eggs
Of beasts as clumsy in the legs
As *Proto-* and *Triceratops*,
And run, like gangster from the cops,

To some safe vantage-point from which
It could enjoy its plunder rich.
Cleverer far than any fox
Or STANLEY in the witness box
It was a *VERY GREAT SUCCESS.*
No egg was safe from it unless
Retained within its mother's womb,
And so the Reptiles met their doom.

The Dinosaurs were most put out
And bitterly complained about
The way their eggs, of giant size,
Were eaten up before their eyes,
Before they had a chance to hatch,
By a beast they couldn't catch.

This awful carnage could not last;
The age of *Archosaurs* was past.
They went as broody as a hen
When all her eggs are pinched by men.
Older they grew, and sadder yet,
But still no offspring could they get.
Until at last the fearful time, as
Yet unguessed by *Struthiomimus*
Arrived, when no more eggs were laid,
And then at last he was afraid.
He could not learn to climb with ease
To reach the birds' nests in the trees,
And though he followed round and round
Some funny furry things he found,
They never laid an egg—not once.
It made him feel an awful dunce.
So, thin beyond all recognition,
He died at last of inanition.

MORAL

This story has a simple moral
With which the wise will hardly quarrel;
Remember that it scarcely ever
Pays to be too bloody clever.

But perhaps the matter is best summed up by Cuppy,[46] 'the Age
of Reptiles ended because it had gone on long enough and it was all a
mistake in the first place'.

L

15 : Modern Mammals

The extinction of the dinosaurs and their allies left life on land much as it had been at the end of the Triassic, but with one important difference: true mammals had developed in the interim. These small insectivorous or carnivorous animals were completely warm-blooded; they were covered in hair, and not only suckled their young but had developed placental reproduction. And they were intelligent. This was probably the key to their subsequent success.

The relative size of the braincase in the mammals indicates their greatly enlarged cerebral hemispheres and cerebellum as compared with their reptilian predecessors (Fig. 30e–h). The enlargement of the braincase was associated with a rearrangement of the jaw apparatus. The lower bar of the synapsid temporal opening flared out to become the zygomatic arch, the post-orbital bar was broken down and a sagittal crest developed, extending the area of attachment for the powerful jaw muscles. The lower jaw was a single bone and articulated directly with the squamosal. This direct articulation of the jaw with the cranium gave the jaw mechanism the potentiality for greater versatility of movement and greater strength of action. Apart from the above structures relating exclusively to the skull, the mammalian skeleton is noteworthy for its overall conservatism. The only major advance is in the method of growth of the endoskeleton. Active growth takes place in a layer of cartilage, the epiphyseal plate, separating the heads of the bone from the shaft. This type of growth has the particular advantage that the articulating ends of the bones are not concerned with their growth. This differs from the situation in most reptiles, where the articular ends of the bones are covered by cartilage which is being continually replaced by bone. It is obviously advantageous not to have the articular surface as the main growing point. The evolution of epiphyseal growth, which is also found in the birds and surprisingly enough in the rhynchocephalian lizards, has a further consequence in that with the ossification of the epiphyseal plates no further increase in size is possible. Once the animals reach maturity, their size is limited; this contrasts with many reptiles, which continue to grow throughout life. Mammalian limbs show a large variety of specialisations reflecting differences in locomotion. One extreme is seen in the bats, which fly by means of their elongated fingers bearing a thin membrane. The problems discussed in relation to the pterosaurs and birds apply here also, and as with the former the bats cannot effectively compete directly with the birds. The bats are successful as they occupy an ecological niche not already taken by the birds, just as the birds were able to evolve because they did not originally compete directly with the pterosaurs. With the exception of the fruit-eating flying foxes, bats are twilight feeders. Other modifications of mammalian limbs are concerned with specialisations for power or speed, as exemplified by the digging animals such as badgers and anteaters and the runners such as deer, horses and cheetahs (see Chapter 4). Most mammals fall between these two extremes and many retain essentially primitive limbs which are capable of a large range of movements. Perhaps associated with this variability of limb structure, the form of mammalian teeth and jaws shows equal variation. This directly reflects the diet of the animals concerned. Although the mammalian skeleton as a whole is marked by its extreme conservatism, the changes in the limbs, teeth and jaws have enabled the mammals to occupy a wide range of ecological niches.[15]

Adaptive Radiation

The evolution o f the modern mammals provides an illustration of the application of a k ind of Parkinson's Law to the natural world. Life (like work) expands t o fill all the available space (time). The clearest example of this is to be found in the Tertiary faunas of South America. At the beginning of the Tertiary, South America was cut off from the rest of the world with a small faun a of condylarths, primitive ungulates and marsupials. The subsequent radiation of the South American mammals paralleled to an astonishing degree the evolution that was taking place quite independently in the rest of the world (Fig. 41). The marsupials were the main carnivores and even a m arsupial 'sabre-tooth tiger' evolved. The still extant shrew-like caenole stid marsupials filled the niche of the insectivores. Among the herbivores such animals as *Thomashuxleya* were similar to the contemporary prim itive artiodactyls. The Sou th American ungulates gave rise to th e rhinoceros-like tox odonts, both running and graviportal types. The typotheres, derived from the same stock, filled the ecological niche of the rodents and lagomorphs. The entylonychids paralleled the cha licotheres, the macrauchenid litopterns, the camels and llamas, th e proterothere

FIG. 41. South American mammals

a. *Theosodon*, a macrauchenid litoptern ('llama'); b. *Paedotherium*, a typothere ('rodent'); c. *Toxodon*, toxodont ('rhinoceros'); d. *Prothylocynus*, marsupial carnivore; e. *Homalodotherium*, entylonychid ('chalicothere'); f. *Thoatherium*, proterothere litoptern ('horse'); g. *Protypotherium*, typothere ('rodent'); h. *Rhynchippus* notoungulate ('running rhinoceros'); i. *Pyrotherium*, pyrothere ('elephant'); j. *Thylacosmilus*, marsupial sabre-tooth.

lipoterns the horses. Even the 'elephants' seem to have been represented by the pyrotheres. Unique to South America were the armadilloes and sloths, culminating in the giant glyptodons and ground sloths, the latter domesticated by man until quite recently.

During the Pliocene, and occasionally during the Miocene, an intermittent land connection was established between North and South America allowing a number of forest-dwelling animals to reach the south. These included the primates, porcupines, peccaries and several other small groups. With the Pleistocene, however, a freeway was established through Central America, which allowed the northern faunas to sweep in and resulted in the mass extinction of virtually the entire endemic fauna. Only the small marsupials, such as the caeno-lestids and opossums, and the armadilloes, anteaters and sloths have survived. This same pattern is now being repeated in Australia, where man and his introduced fauna are making vast inroads into the endemic marsupial fauna. A fauna which includes some incredible examples of parallelism: the marsupial mole, the marsupial flying squirrel, which parallels the gliding or 'flying lemur' *Galeopithecus*, the cat-like Tasmanian Devil, and the thylacine 'wolf'.

Since a discussion of the variety of adaptations to particular environments in the main groups of mammals would require a further volume, it seems more sensible to examine the major adaptations to environment achieved by the mammals. The modifications of the basic mammalian form relate primarily to the limbs and dentition. However, if the specialisations of the limbs are taken as basic criteria, a series of anomalous situations result. The cheetah and its prey are both special-ised for running at high speed; the anteater and the badger are modified for digging, but their habits are in all other respects entirely different.

By contrast, the form of the dentition gives an accurate indication of the animal's diet and is, therefore, a more trustworthy guide to its way of life. Mammals can be classified on the basis of their diet. This classification, however, will split up natural phyletic groups into different categories and at the same time will unite unrelated animals sharing the same type of food. The advantage of this approach is that it emphasises the incredible evolutionary versatility of the modern mammals. Such a systematic arrangement of the mammalian dentition has been prepared by Dr. Karen Hiiemäe[80] and the following account, with minor exceptions, is based on her work and is included here with her kind permission.

Diet and Dentition

The primitive mammalian dentition is characterised by the presence of different types of teeth: anteriorly there are three pairs of incisors, whose main function is gripping and pulling; these are followed by a pair of canines for stabbing and tearing; the posterior teeth (the premolars, primitively four pairs, and the molars, three pairs) are used for crushing, grinding or cutting up food (Fig. 42a–c). As in the more primitive vertebrates, the lower and upper teeth alternate with each other, and in the occlusion of the teeth there are two essential components: firstly apposition, where the occlusal surfaces come into direct contact with and crush the food; and secondly shear, where there is a cutting action between the ridges or edges of the teeth. These two components of apposition or shear will be exaggerated at one another's expense, depending on the type of diet of the animal.

The earliest and most primitive of modern mammals were insectivorous, feeding on insects and grubs. In this group there are two types of molar teeth, the tribosphenic or trituberculosectorial, the more usual, and the zalambodont, found in the tenrec, where there is a W-shaped pattern of cusps. The incisors and canines are very sharp and the cusps of the molars form sharp points which serve to pierce the chitinous exoskeletons of their prey. The bats, which capture insects on the wing, have this same basic primitive dentition. The tree-shrews, which are generally included in the primates in spite of recent doubts about such an assignation, also possess this same type of primitive generalised dentition. Several groups of mammal have become adapted to a highly specialised insect diet of ants and termites. This involved the evolution of strong claws for digging into the ants' nests or termite hills and long sticky whip-like tongues for collecting the insects. The mouth was reduced to a small round orifice at the end of a long snout and the teeth to simple pegs or, as in the case of the South American anteaters, were lost altogether. Animals adopting this way of life include representatives of five different orders: the egg-laying monotreme the *Echidna* or spiny anteater, the marsupial aardwolf, the Asian scaly anteater the Pangolin, the South American anteater, and the archaic tubulodentate, the aardwark of southern Africa. None of these groups are in any way related to one another, but they have occupied the same ecological niche and have independently evolved the same morphological features as an adaptation to diet.

Terrestrial Carnivores

The carnivores feed on animal flesh, and their prey consists of birds, small mammals and—in the case of the larger types—the ungulates. All carnivores have first to catch and kill their prey. This can be accomplished in one of two ways, either by slashing the hide and eviscerating the animal or by severing the vessels of the neck. Thereafter the muscles and tendons have to be torn from the bones and chopped up into manageable pieces. Carnivores are equipped with powerful clawed limbs for holding and tearing at their victims, and with an anterior battery of biting and piercing teeth. The anterior teeth are backed up by highly specialised carnassial teeth (Fig. 42d). 'These are modified cheek teeth which have developed into elongated serrated-edged cutting blades, and when in action the lower and upper close together like the blades of scissors'[80]. In the living fissiped carnivores the carnassials are developed from the fourth upper premolars and the first lower molars. Among the extinct carnivorous deltatheridians, the cat-like oxyaenids, the major carnassials developed from the first upper and second lower molars, although there were accessory sectorial teeth equivalent to the fissiped carnassials. The closely related hyaena-like hyaenodonts had three pairs of carnassials, the principal pair being formed by the second upper and third lower molars, with accessory pairs as in the oxyaenids. The specialised carnivorous condylarths, the dog-like mesonychid creodonts, had lower teeth with a shearing form but apparently no shearing function! The dental requirements of an efficient carnivore include a shearing dentition, and this was independently evolved in three separate mammalian orders—the Deltatheridia, Condylarthra and Carnivora.

One carnivorous group, in the popular sense of the term but not yet mentioned, are the blood drinkers, the most notorious example being the vampire bat. The incisors are razor-sharp and are used to shave off the skin until the blood begins to well up, whereupon anticoagulants are injected into the wound by the grooved upper incisors. Since these bats lap up the blood, it is important that the supply should not be halted by clotting.

Aquatic Carnivores

Aquatic carnivores have quite different problems from their terrestrial relatives. In most aquatic, and especially the marine, carnivores the dentition is secondarily simplified, in some cases reverting to the extreme homodont condition seen in the common dolphin, where the dentition is enormously increased so that the tooth row consists of dozens of small, needle-sharp, closely packed teeth, ideally suited to gripping and preventing the escape of slippery fish. However, the seals still retain incisors and canines, and the last incisor is frequently caniniform. The cheek teeth are simplified to three longitudinally aligned cusps, and again serve to hold fish. The dolphins and whales, which feed mainly on cephalopods, do not require a fish-trap type of dentition and their teeth are fewer, well separated and more massive affairs. Since modern cephalopods are essentially soft-bodied, an effective battery of teeth is hardly necesssry and the beaked dolphin is edentulous; the sperm whale has no functional upper teeth and even its lower ones are almost submerged in the gums. However, one line of cephalopod-feeders retained its teeth and used them on its fellows. Animals such as the killer whales are voracious feeders on seals and dolphins and are also reputed to be partial to the tongues of the giant whalebone whales, which they rip out.

The walruses, related to the seals, have become bivalve-eaters; their upper canines form long projecting tusks which are used for grubbing up shells from the sea bed, while the cheek teeth are reduced to simple rounded pegs for crushing the shells.

Another source of food for aquatic carnivores is the plankton, especially the planktonic crustaceans or krill. To ingest an adequate quantity, large volumes of water must be taken into the mouth and then expelled, leaving the trapped krill behind. The so-called crab-eating seal achieves this by using its sharply tricuspid interdigitating teeth as a sieve; but the most extreme example is the whalebone whale. These whales, being edentulous mammals, have a large fringe of whalebone derived from the oral mucosa, hanging from the upper jaw. The krill are trapped within the whalebone and then retrieved and swallowed. Despite intensive investigation, exactly how the krill are retrieved prior to swallowing remains a mystery.

Jaws of Carnivores

In discussing the diet of carnivorous mammals attention has been focused only on the dentition; but this is an integral part of the entire jaw apparatus and should therefore be considered in conjunction with the articulation of the jaw and its musculature. In typical terrestrial carnivores, in which the action of the jaws is a simple scissor one, the opening and shutting of the mouth must be in one plane for the carnassials to shear effectively. The articular condyle of the mandible is orientated transversely, and so severely limits lateral play of the jaws; its surface is strongly convex and fits into a deep concavity in the squamosal, which develops bony hook-like flanges both in front of and behind the articular fossa, thus ensuring that the lower jaw is rigidly held in its socket (Fig. 42e). This is essential, since oftener than not the victim will struggle violently. The Temporalis and Masseter are massively developed, since they are the muscles responsible for the powerful closing movements of the jaw. The Pterygoid muscles which are primarily responsible for lateral movements, are consequently small.

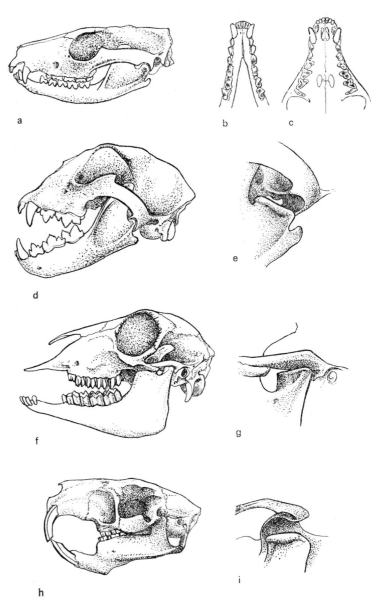

FIG. 42. a–c. primitive mammalian skull (marsupial): a. lateral view,
b. dorsal view of lower jaw, and c. palatal of upper; d, e. advanced
carnivore (cat) showing: d. scissor-action of teeth, and e. tight jaw articulation; f, g. advanced herbivore (sheep) showing: f. ridged teeth, diastema,
and g. loose flat articulation; h, i. advanced herbivore (coypu) showing:
h. chisel-like incisors, diastema, and i. elongation of articulation
antero-posteriorly.

Herbivores—Browsers and Grazers

A herbivorous diet poses fundamentally different problems. Most importantly, the animals must ingest greater quantities of food per unit body weight, as vegetable matter has a low protein content compared with meat. Moreover the plant material has to be crushed to break down the cellulose cell walls and, since they contain a high proportion of silica, this causes excessive wear on the teeth. Simple tribosphenic teeth would be quite inadequate to deal with such material, and these have become highly modified in herbivores. The shear component is reduced in favour of excessive apposition, and the crowns of the teeth usually develop ridges—the lophodont condition—to give a more effective grinding surface to the teeth. Some have molars with a bubbly surface, the bunodont condition. The premolars become molarised, thus extending the working surface of the dentition. These molarised teeth become high crowned, or hypsodont, and may be persisently growing. Finally the crowns are covered by cement, so that with the differential wear of three tissues of differing hardnesses, enamel, dentine and cement, a sharply ridged surface is always maintained.

In the odd-toed ungulates, the perissodactyls, especially in the series illustrating the evolution of the horse, there is a gradual sequence from the primitive tribosphenic condition to a simple lophodont one, such as is present in the living tapir. This evolutionary sequence can be traced to its culmination in the exceedingly elaborate folding of the enamel ridges in the hypsodont teeth of the modern horse, in which moreover it is hardly possible to distinguish the molars from the premolars. Throughout this series the anterior teeth are used for gathering or cropping; between these teeth and the posterior grinding cheek teeth there is a space or diastema, in the region of which food collects before being passed back by the tongue for grinding. From the dentition it is evident that the early horses, like the living tapirs, were browsers, whereas the development of a more complex pattern indicates the ability to deal with such siliceous material as grasses (i.e. to graze). Essentially the same evolutionary history can be traced in the even-toed ungulates, the artiodactyls, which reached their acme in the ruminants. The most advanced of this latter group lost the upper incisors and canines, which were replaced by a keratinised cropping pad; the lower incisors and incisiform canines were retained. The teeth in the advanced genera are hypsodont and the crowns show a complex pattern of ridges with cement on their occlusal surfaces; there is also complete molarisation of the premolars (Fig. 42f). Most of the ruminants have horns or antlers but one group, the chevrotains or water deer, do not; they have long sharp dagger-like upper canines, which are clearly for defence and display and certainly not for meat-eating (reminiscent of the early ornithischian dinosaur *Heterodontosaurus*).

Elephants

A further group, which illustrates an alternative method of coping with the problem of excessive wear is the Proboscidea. The difficulties of a herbivorous diet reach their extreme with this particular group, since by virtue of their size the amount of food to be consumed must be proportionately greater. For any unit increase in the linear dimensions of the animal, the volume will increase by its cube. Hence the extra amount of food required will be increased by the cube; and yet by the same token the working area of the teeth—the occlusal surface—would increase by only the square. The earliest elephants were only about 2 ft. high; they had procumbent incisors for grubbing up food which occluded against the lips of a short mobile snout, a pair of upper incisors formed short tusks, while the cheek teeth were simple bunodont. With an increase in size, both the upper and lower incisors and also the mobile snout increased in length so that the animal was still able to reach the ground for its food. At the same time the cusp pattern of the molars and premolars became more complex by the addition of extra cusps posteriorly, and the teeth also became more hypsodont. The tooth row was shortened and brought nearer to the squamosal-dentary joint so that the musculature could act more effectively in crushing the food. With the shortening of the tooth row and the increase in size of the individual teeth, the full complement of teeth were no longer used simultaneously, but instead the eruption of the more posterior teeth was progressively delayed, until the stage was reached in the modern elephants where only one tooth is in use at any one time. The teeth erupted from the back but they were brought into use obliquely, so that almost every particle of hard tissue was utilised. Once the snout had become greatly elongated, the mobile proboscis became the main food-gathering organ. This made the lower incisors redundant, and they were quickly lost. The upper incisors were retained as the familiar tusks, while the proboscis, no longer supported by a long mandibular symphysis or procumbent incisors, simply hung down (and this is how the elephant *actually* got its trunk). The pattern of development in the proboscideans in all probability was repeated in all the different evolutionary lineages. The only distinguishing feature that separates the different lineages and allows them to be recognised, is the slight difference in the ways in which the pattern of cusps is elaborated. In the trilophodont line there are accessory cusps or conules that are formed between the main cusps, so that when they are worn down they give a characteristic trefoil outline. The surviving line retained well marked transverse fissures between the row of cusps. In the browsing American mastodon, which had two teeth in each half jaw at any one time, there were only two large rounded cusps in each row; in the later grazing types these rows became much narrower, forming dental plates which when they were worn down gave a pattern of transverse ridges. As with the advanced ungulates, these ridges were retained by virtue of the differential wear of the enamel, dentine and cementum. The dietary history of the elephants seems to follow that of the ungulates in that there was a transition from soft to tougher plant material.

Herbivores—Gnawers and Nibblers

In contrast to the browsers and grazers are the gnawers and nibblers. Nibbling is a mode of life enjoyed by the advanced tritylodont paramammals at the end of the Trias, by the true mammalian multituberculates during the Cretaceous and Eocene, and by several groups of Palaeocene primates. The gnawing mammals have permanently-growing incisors, essentially self-sharpening chisels, and they chip off particles of food which are then passed back to the grinding cheek teeth characterised by an intricate pattern of enamel ridges (Fig. 42h). Here the food is either pounded or ground. The living rodents and the unrelated lagomorphs, which can be easily distinguished by their two pairs of upper incisors *in tandem* rather than the single pair of the true rodents, show such a degree of parallelism that for a long time it was thought that rabbits and hares were rodents. The extinct rodent-like typotheres from South America also demonstrate this same degree of adaptation to this particular mode of life. Even the living aye-aye of Madagascar, which is a rodent-like lemur, shows this same type of adaptation.

Jaws of Herbivores

The jaw mechanism in herbivorous mammals is predominantly concerned with apposition as opposed to shear. In the advanced ungulates the Temporalis and Masseter muscles are much less well developed than in the carnivores; the opening and closing of the mouth is not so very important, and in fact the gape is exceedingly small compared with that of any carnivore. In spite of the great depth of the ramus of the mandible, the mandibular condyle is ridiculously small in proportion. It is small and flat and articulates with an ill-defined fossa, so allowing extensive lateral movements of the jaws which are associated with the grinding chewing movements (Fig. 42g). The

Pterygoid muscles are very strongly developed, and are responsible for lateral movements of the lower jaws.

The arrangement in the gnawing forms is quite different, since the dentition has to perform two separate and highly specialised functions, the gnawing action of the incisors and the grinding of the cheek teeth. When the incisors are in use the lower jaw is brought forward; when the cheek teeth are grinding, the mandible is retracted. So the jaw apparatus is modified to allow extensive movement in the anterior-posterior direction (Fig. 42i). The mandibular condyle is elongate, and the superficial part of the Masseter muscle and the posterior fibres of the Temporalis are orientated so that they can produce extensive protrusion and retraction of the mandible. Although this appears to be the main movement in the rodent type of jaw, Dr. Karen Hiiemäe[79] has recently demonstrated that the movement of the cheek teeth during grinding is much more complex than had been previously suspected. In the rat for example, there is a rotational pounding movement which has an essential lateral component. The need for an extreme modification of the jaw apparatus to allow the mandible to slide to and fro has tended to overshadow, and thus obscure, the fact that the functioning of the cheek teeth was based not on a simple to and fro type of movement but on one more normal for a herbivore, viz. a pounding action with a lateral component.

Omnivores

In any dietary classification there must be a group including those animals that will eat most things and whose dentition is not really modified for any particular type of food. Among the basically herbivorous animals the pigs fall into this category, whilst from the carnivorous side the bears do.

The pigs and their allies are artiodactyls and, although they root up plant food, they can in many ways be considered omnivorous, because they eat carrion. The lower incisors are procumbent for digging, the canines are reverted and are used as weapons, and the cheek teeth have the basic number of four cusps but the enamel is considerably crinkled to give the multicuspid bunodont condition. This latter development reaches its extreme in the last molars of the warthog which appear proboscidean!

Some carnivores have changed their diet to an omnivorous or wholly herbivorous type. The occlusal surfaces of the carnassial teeth and molars become expanded and at the same time develop the accessory cuspules or bunodont teeth. This is well seen in the bears and in the exclusively vegetarian raccoons and pandas.

These two groups, the pigs and bears, are secondarily omnivorous. The primary omnivores are basically large insectivores; the dentition remains singularly primitive so enabling the animals concerned to deal with a great variety of foodstuffs. The only important change in the dentition is the development of extra cusps on the molars. This development characterises the primates which, although unable to compete on equal terms with the more highly specialised herbivores or carnivores, remained adaptable.

History of Carnivores

The mammals as a whole were remarkably adaptable and whatever basic stock was present in an area, it would, given time, radiate to fill all the available ecological niches. This is clearly demonstrated by the way in which similar dentitions are evolved by animals that are not at all related to one another but develop comparable modifications for the same basic requirements. But the feature which is always claimed to be the ultimate key to mammalian success is their intelligence. Throughout the history of the vertebrates the herbivorous types have been evolutionary dead ends. A herbivore has to defend itself or escape, whereas a carnivore in order to survive has to be able to find and catch its prey. The requirements of a hunter seem to provide a stimulus for evolution. This is well illustrated in the history of the carnivorous mammals. During the early part of the Tertiary the main carnivores were the deltatherids and condylarths.

These two groups filled most of the ecological niches now occupied by living carnivores. The deltatherids include the hyaenodonts, the early members of which ranged in size from that of a weasel to that of a fox, they retained the primitive mammalian dentition, and had short delicate limbs. The advanced hyaenodonts had a short neck, long trunk and powerful limbs, and to judge from their general proportions and dentition seem to have been scavengers. The second group of deltatherids were the oxyaenids, with large skulls but short faces and short, stout limbs. These animals were cat-like and seem to have been adapted for pouncing on their prey. The condylarths include the primitive arctocyonids, which gave rise to the carnivorous bear-like types, and also the most highly specialised of the archaic carnivores, the dog-like mesonychids. This group, like the dogs, had become modified for running its prey down, and had evolved similar adaptations for a cursorial habit.

Contemporary with these four main groups of archaic carnivores or creodonts was a further group of carnivorous mammal, the miacids. These were characterised by the possession of only one pair of carnassial teeth, the fourth upper premolar and the first lower molar; they were lightly built with rather short faces. In one feature they contrasted with all the other carnivores of the time: their cranium was rounded and capacious, and the sagittal crests were consequently reduced, since the expanded braincase provided ample area for the attachment of the jaw musculature.

In mid-Tertiary times, and in particular with the spread of grasslands, the herbivores became adapted not only for grazing but also for speed in running. In these new circumstances the creodonts were simply unable to keep up with their food, except for the advanced hyaenodonts which were scavengers, and as a result they simply died out. Since it was not possible to out-run the herbivores or approach them unseen across open country, there was a premium on brains; only animals with a high degree of intelligence could hope to survive. The miacids alone were suitably equipped, and from them there evolved the two main lines of the modern carnivores, the cats and the dogs.

Cats

The cats are noted for their stealth and cunning. They are able to creep up to their prey and then pounce. The most primitive members of the cat family are the forest-dwelling civets, the viverrids, which are not unlike the miacids. During the Pliocene the modern scavenging hyaenas, which were a side branch of the civets, appeared and filled the niche formerly occupied by the hyaenodonts. They are digitigrade, like the dogs, and are therefore popularly considered to be closer to the dogs than to the cats. The true cats have retractile claws and soft padded feet; these animals first appeared in the Oligocene, and two basic types can be recognised—the biting cats and the stabbing cats. There were also the so-called 'false sabre-tooths' which had upper canines longer than in the modern cats but shorter than in the sabre-tooths. In cross-section the canines were exactly intermediate between the narrow blade of the sabre and the more elliptical biting tooth. These false sabre-tooths may have been close to the common stock from which the main lines diverged. Some of them were clearly cursorial; their proportions were comparable to those of the cheetah, and in the hind limbs the digits were reduced to four, as in the dogs. In this they contrasted with the true sabre-tooths, which had very massive limbs, particularly the forelimbs which presumably, held down large prey. The early sabre tooths had bony flanges on the mandible which protected the sabres. In the latest forms the canines projected well below the mandible, even with the mouth closed. These stabbing cats were successful well into Pleistocene times. Their main prey were the gigantic herbivorous mammals that seemed to reach the acme of their development during the Pleistocene, as shown by Leakey's discoveries in central Africa. The sabre-tooths were obviously well equipped for dealing with large, comparatively ungainly prey, but were not so adept at hunting the more agile of the ungulates. In fact the sabre-tooths did not require much intelligence for their survival just so long as there was a sufficiency of large animals on which to feed.

As an illustration of the importance of intelligence, in the famous Rancho La Brea tar-pits in Los Angeles the true modern biting cat, the Californian lion, is outnumbered 30 to 1 by the sabre-tooths. The modern-type cats which fed on agile prey and so needed to be intelligent to feed at all, were also capable of realising that the apparent abundance of food from animals trapped in the tar-pits was treacherous, and therefore it was a place to be avoided.

Finally, it is a notable fact that the smaller cats are more successful now than at any time in their previous history, by virtue of their association with man. The Pleistocene explosive evolution of rats and mice, undoubtedly related to the success of our own species, would have provided an excellent opportunity for the small cats which hunt by stealth. The retiring nature of the cat would have meant that it would have been easily tolerated by man, even eventually being encouraged, by being allowed to scavenge. The odd association between cat and man must have begun in this way. The uncommunicativeness of the cat, who walks by himself, has frequently been considered mysterious and the animal's superiority divine! The personality of the cat is simply an inheritance of animals that could survive only by the intelligent use of their faculties in hunting prey that in the normal course of events they could never hope to catch—stealth and cunning are the hall-marks of the cat's success. Its association with man, or rather woman, is perhaps a measure of the cat's intelligence. The only price they have paid is that common to all civilised communities, dental disease as a consequence of soft (frequently tinned) cooked foods on which, at least in this country, they mainly subsist!

Dogs

The other line of modern carnivores includes the small forest-dwellers—the weasels and stoats, wolverines, otters and badgers, all of which were established by the end of the Miocene. These all have stocky limbs and again are not dissimilar to the miacids. They also gave rise to the raccoons and the bears; but the main line of advance was not towards an omnivorous diet as in these lines, but to the fully cornivorous one of the dogs. Unlike the other carnivores the dogs run their prey down. The radius and ulna are locked to prevent rotation of the forearm, the digits are parallel and reduced to four. These animals are digitigrade and are adapted for long sustained running. The cerebral cortex is considerably elaborated, indicating a high level of intelligence. Moreover dogs cannot out-run most ungulates, but they succeed by hunting in packs and by employing complicated stratagems which panic the prey until it wears itself out and falls an easy victim to the pack. The dog is fundamentally a social animal, and as with all higher social animals, there is a hierarchy in the community. The pack has a leader and the whole society is stratified. Since the dog is a social animal, communication is all-important, if the hunt is to be effective, because the situation will vary from second to second. This is probably the reason man knows more about and more fully appreciates the dog. Indeed Pavlov's later work on the psychology of dogs demonstrated that the same basic temperaments or personality types into which Hippocrates classified men were applicable to dogs in an identical way. On this subject Sargant[183] wrote:

'Thirty years of research convinced Pavlov that the four basic temperaments of his dogs approximated closely to those differentiated in man by the ancient Greek physician Hippocrates. Though various blends of basic temperamental pattern appeared in Pavlov's dogs, they could be distinguished as such, rather than as new temperamental categories.

The first of these four corresponded with Hippocrates' 'choleric' type, which Pavlov named the 'strong excitory'. The second corresponded with Hippocrates' 'sanguine' temperament; Pavlov named it 'lively', the dogs of this type being of a more balanced temperament. The normal response to imposed stresses or conflict situations by both these types was one of increased excitement and more aggressive behaviour. But whereas the 'choleric', or 'strong excitory' dog would often turn so wild as to be completely out of hand, the 'sanguine' or 'lively' dog's reactions to identical stresses were purposeful and controlled.

In the other two main temperamental types of dog, imposed stresses and conflict situations were met with more passivity or 'inhibition', rather than aggressive responses. The more stable of these two inhibitory temperaments was described by Pavlov as the 'calm imperturbable type', the 'phlegmatic' type of Hippocrates. The remaining temperament identified by Pavlov corresponds with Hippocrates' 'melancholic' classification; Pavlov named it the 'weak inhibitory' type. He found that a dog of this type shows a constitutional tendency to meet anxieties and conflict with passivity and avoidance of tension. Any strong experimental stress imposed on its nervous system reduces it to a state of brain inhibition and 'fear paralysis'. '

M

This remarkable identity of canine and human personalities would seem to be an intrinsic feature of group hunting predators. The group must work as a unit; but for this it is vital that there should be a hierarchy with a leader which will give the society coherence. In contrast to the majority of primate communities, the main activity of canine and human societies is killing. It may well be, as Fiennes[60] has suggested, that man 'the most dangerous, ruthless, prodigal killer of all time . . . could not but be trailed by a host of pariah animals, which would subsist on his leavings'. In fact both early man and dog worked with the same end in view and moreover probably employed the same stratagems. Since dogs must have been familiar scavengers around human settlements, there must have been many occasions on which the puppies were reared by man. Furthermore, like man, the dog is a highly adaptable social animal, and would have taken easily to domestication. This is especially so since the tasks required of him were the very same as those for which he and his ancestors had been adapted over the years, namely those involved in hunting. Here, at least initially, there was really no change in the dog's way of life; only the hunting pack now included man. There developed a mutualism that was of advantage to both species, and it is difficult to assign the credit to either one species or the other—both were highly intelligent, both were highly adaptable and both were in societies organised on exactly the same principles for achieving the same ends. As man's way of life has undergone changes, so too the dog has been able to adapt himself, with the aid undoubtedly of a little selective breeding. With the establishment of settled human communities there were already house dogs, sheep dogs for herding, and hounds for hunting. Since the basic instincts of the dog coincide with those of man, it is easy to understand the close association that has developed between these two groups of social predators. Being social animals, both man and dog find communication of vital concern, and thus the intelligence of the dog is more easily recognised by our species than is that of the probably equally sagacious, but sly and secretive, cat.

In any event the ability to think is not confined to our own species; it characterises other groups of mammals. The only difference is one of degree.

16 : Man—The Weapon Maker

The evolution and origin of man present no real problems. In spite of the fact that the early stages were spent in forests and these are notoriously bad for fossilisation, sufficient material is known to allow the main evolution to be adequately documented. The later evolution is much easier, as our ancestors inhabited open country. Indeed, the only serious problem in the study of fossil man is where to draw the boundary between man and non-man. The advanced fossil primates grade imperceptibly into mankind; where the boundary is drawn is a question of personal taste.[29,86,128]

Arboreal Adaptations

The primates are first known from the Cretaceous and were small insectivores.[193] The difficulty in defining the primates is that they have retained all the basic primitive features of the early mammals. In essence they are characterised by remaining generalised and not becoming specialised for any particular mode of life. The key to their success has been their adaptability, their own 'specialisation' being that they have remained unspecialised. Whereas the majority of mammals abandoned life in the trees at the dawn of the Tertiary, the primates stayed where they were. All the structural changes that link man to small insectivorous mammals are the direct consequence of these primitive animals becoming better adapted to an arboreal existence.[35] The sequence of changes that can be traced seem to be merely the result of the increase in size of the primates, and Simons[186] has pointed out that all the living groups of higher primates have passed through similar structural stages, in many cases independently of one another.

An animal the size of a squirrel can run along branches and twigs with considerable ease, but for animals of much greater weight the thinner branches will not afford adequate support. This means that the animal will have to jump from branch to branch. In order to accomplish this efficiently the eyes need to be able to focus on the same object. The eyes gradually become positioned towards the front of the skull, so that both fields of vision overlap to give the animal binocular vision, with the result that the animal is able to judge distances accurately. The rotation of the eyes so that they face forwards has important consequences as far as the skull is concerned. The jaw musculature bulges forwards when the animal bites and since the anterior part will impinge on the orbital region it is necessary for the eyes to be protected. This is achieved by the secondary formation of the postorbital bar (lost during the late evolution of the paramammals) and subsequently a complete bony wall. This new formation, however, is developed from different elements in different groups of primate.

As the capacity to see improved, the sense of smell became diminished in importance, The nasal apparatus, and hence the snout, was markedly reduced so that the face became flat. The mandible was shortened and the dentition of necessity reduced. The improvement in vision must go hand in hand with similar improvements in muscular coordination and the sense of balance, as the animal is living in a 'three-dimensional' medium.

Further key adaptations are the opposable first digits, especially the thumb, and the replacement of claws by flat nails. This is significant on two counts: it enables the animal to grasp branches and also to handle objects. The forearm retains its primitive mobility, the radius and ulna being able to rotate on one another. This means that forearm and hand can be used not only in locomotion but also for manipulating the environment. With still further increase in size, the main mode of progression, typified by the orang and gibbon, is by swinging through the branches. For this the opposable thumb is of prime import, but this type of locomotion has further consequences. The fore limbs gradually become longer and stronger, since they have to bear the whole weight of the body. The clavicle or collar bone, which was an element in the shoulder girdle of the crossopterygian fish but is either merely vestigial or completely lost in many mammals, became important in helping to give extra attachments to the musculature of the upper arm and neck which take the weight. The strength of the arms in taking the weight of the body is well seen in human babies. The hanging of the body with the arms at the side and raised above the head also leads to changes in the proportions of the trunk in that the chest becomes wider than it is deep unlike the situation in normal quadrupeds. The higher primates are characteristically flat or barrel-chested.

Perhaps the major result of the adoption of a brachiating habit is the simple fact that the animal will hang upright. The most obvious effect of the brachiating habit is that of the gradual divergence in function and form of the fore and hind limbs. The forearm and hand become more and more used for handling objects as well as for loco-motion. When such animals come down on the ground, their gait may be essentially bipedal. The hind limbs are for walking and, although they may revert to a type of quadrupedal gait by allowing their long arms to touch the ground, they are, as Dr. Jane Goodall[69] has observed in chimpanzees, perfectly able to run on their hind limbs carrying objects in their arms.

For any further advance it is essential that having reached this level of organisation they finally abandon the arboreal habitat. Otherwise the animals may continue to become even more highly adapted to the brachiating habit and reach the stage of such extreme brachiators as the gibbon and the extinct *Oreopithecus* with their inordinately long forearms. However, even with these extreme types, the higher primates are all characterised by the development of comparable adaptations to an arboreal existence. The great increase in the brain's size, and especially those parts concerned with the coordination of what the eye sees and the hand does, the visual and motor cortex, is a direct consequence of the evolution of binocular vision and the manipulative hand with its opposable thumb.

Early Primates

In a general way the living primates show a scale of organisation from insectivores to man. The tree shrew *Tupaia* from Borneo, although denied primate status by some authors, nevertheless represents the type of organisation from which all the higher primates must have been derived. This animal differs only slightly from the insectivores, but has very mobile fingers and toes used for grasping. The primitive primate *Plesiadapis* (Fig. 43a, b) and its allies from the Palaeocene of Europe and North America seem to belong to this particular grade of organisation; there is no postorbital bar developed and the clawed fingers are clearly well adapted for grasping objects. During Palaeocene and early Eocene times the majority of primates filled the ecological niche now occupied by the rodents and were specialised for gnawing, with chisel-like incisors and a wide diastema between them and the cheek teeth. As Simons[188] comments, 'It seems reasonable to suppose that these early primates started their evolutionary careers in competition for some kind of nibblers' and gnawers' niche in the warm forests. They were not successful; before the middle of the Eocene all three chisel-toothed prosimian families had become extinct. Perhaps they were put out of business by the rodents, which became abundant as these prosimians were dying out'. Nevertheless these animals show a number

Fig. 43. Early primates. a, b. *Plesiadapis*: **a.** reconstruction, **b.** restoration (Palaeocene); c, d. *Smilodectes*: c. restoration, d. reconstruction (Eocene); e, f. *Pliopithecus*: e. reconstruction, f. restoration (Miocene); g–i. *Dryopithecus*: g, h. skull in lateral and anterior views; i. restoration (Miocene–Pliocene). (after Simons).

of similarities to the Eocene lemurs, in the cusp patterns of their cheek teeth and in the structures of their limbs. These animals have the eyes positioned at the front of the head giving the animals binocular vision, the snout is shortened and the cerebral hemispheres are considerably enlarged. The first digits are now opposable and bear flat nails rather than claws. The ancestry of the modern lemurs is quite evidently from these Eocene forms, although the specialisations of the teeth in the living forms had not yet developed. Living lemurs have procumbent lower incisors with a comb-like form. During the Eocene and at the very beginning of the Oligocene the structural advances of the prosimians were further extended in the necrolemurs (Fig. 43c, d). The forebrain was further enlarged, and the eyes now placed on the very front of the face, which was flat. The necrolemurs probably gave rise to the modern tarsiers, which are highly specialised nocturnal arboreal animals. Their eyes are huge and they have developed an extra joint in the hind limb by elongating the ankle bones, the astralagus and calcaneum, enabling the opposable big toe to be retained. At the same time it is likely that the higher primates, the anthropoids, were derived from animals similar to the necrolemurs. The problem as to whether the higher primates evolved from a tree-shrew stage via a tarsioid, or via a lemur and then tarsioid, stage is an academic question, the answer to which depends on how one wishes to classify the various advanced prosimians of the Eocene. In any event, it is evident that there was a gradual structural advance towards the anthropoid condition. In the Oligocene deposits of the Fayum of Egypt the two main groups of the Old World higher primates were already represented, the catarrhines (as opposed to the New World monkeys, the platyrrhines). The basal stock of the Old World monkeys, the cercopithecids, is represented by *Oligopithecus*, while the stock of the hominoids, i.e. apes and men, by *Propliopithecus*. Simons[188] has pointed out that although this genus was for a long time thought to be an ancestral gibbon, it is a much more generalised animal, which 'may well prove to be on or near the line of evolutionary development that led to the living pongids and to man'.

Ramapithecus—the First Hominid

The Miocene period saw the continuation of the line leading to the advanced brachiator *Pliopithecus* (Fig. 43e, f) whose fore and hind limbs were of similar length, in contrast with the gibbon in which the arms are considerably longer than the legs. At the same time, and extending through into the Pliocene period, were a group of lightly built apes, the dryopithecines, which seem to have inhabited open savannah country (Fig. 43g–i). These animals had a somewhat arched dental arcade—

clearly one from which that of man could have derived, if we bear in mind that the human condition is the primitive one and that the parallel tooth rows of the living apes are a later specialisation. However, the canines projected beyond the occlusal level of the other teeth, unlike the situation in man, where they are reduced and incisiform. Although it was felt that these dryopithecines were close to the common stock of apes and man, they were already on the line leading to the apes.

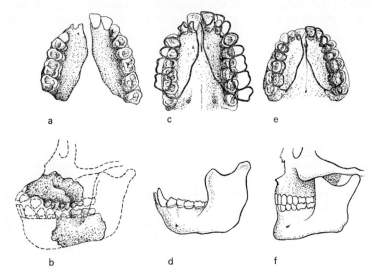

a   c   e

b   d   f

FIG. 44. a, b. *Ramapithecus* (Miocene–Pliocene); c, d. *Pan*, orangutan, with outline of *Ramapithecus* jaw; e, f. *Homo sapiens*, with outline of *Ramapithecus* jaw. (after Simons).

This group of primitive apes lived in communities in open country and had an extensive geographical distribution, ranging from Western Europe and Asia Minor to Egypt, central Africa, northern India and south-west China. The only means of defence available to these highly vulnerable animals were their canines and, presumably, the fact that they could act in concert. In the last few years, Simons has demonstrated that these animals were not a homogeneous assemblage, but that two fundamentally distinct lineages can be recognised. These are the small ape *Dryopithecus* and the human ancestor *Ramapithecus*, which was the size of a chimpanzee and is found in Miocene and Pliocene deposits from Kenya and India.[162,185,187,189,190] Although known only from jaw fragments, it is evident that the face was markedly foreshortened and the teeth were in many respects similar to those of man (Fig. 44).

The incisors were reduced in size compared with those of the modern apes, and the canine was little bigger than the premolars, a characteristically human trait, again contrasting with the strongly developed ape canines. The dental arcade is also characteristically human. On dental characters alone it can be claimed that the human stock was already distinguishable in Miocene times, some twenty million years ago. Since these small, lightly built proto-humans, which must have run about on their hind limbs, seemed even more defenceless than the contemporary dryopithecines, their remarkable future success requires an explanation. The reduction of the canines as weapons must presuppose the existence of an alternative method of defence. Since this was clearly not dependent on the structures of the animals, it suggests that it must have been some part of the external environment, and the most appropriate objects that would come easily to hand would be sticks and stones. It can be tentatively concluded that *Ramapithecus* defended himself in this way, a view supported by Leakey's[119] recent finds of broken ungulate bones from the Miocene of Kenya.

Australopithecus and *'Homo habilis'*

The study of all subsequent finds of fossil 'ape-men' or men is fraught with acrimonious controversy and a nomenclature of inordinate complexity. The plethora of 'species' and 'genera' serves only to confuse what is in essence a fairly simple and straightforward process. The story of the origin of modern man starts with Dart's discovery in 1924 of the skull of an immature animal that he named *Australopithecus africanus* (Fig. 45h, i).[50] To quote Ardrey,[18] 'The 1924 Taung's skull was that of an infant, and Dart's description violated every scientific preconception of the time. His grasp of comparative anatomy led him to project the adult creature as four feet tall, erect in its carriage, bipedal, and with a brain still the size of a gorilla's: as an animal, in other words, halfway between ape and man. Dart further deduced from study of the creature's teeth and habitat that *Australopithecus africanus* had been carnivorous and had led a hunting life.[51] The ape-man had been a transitional being possessing every significant human qualification other than man's big brain'. This interpretation was hailed with a certain amount of derision. The prehistoric neanderthal man had a human brain but a brutish ape-like posture and Piltdown man had a human brain but still retained the jaw of an ape. It was firmly believed that the development of the human brain came first and the changes in the character of his jaws and posture and gait came later. Since Dart had apparently failed to understand this and had got everything back to front, the authorities of his day had no difficulty in dismissing his interpretation out of hand. Time had its revenge. It is now accepted that Dart was entirely correct in his deductions; indeed further discoveries confirmed his prediction. Piltdown was exposed as a clever hoax[137] and Cave[32] has since shown the posture of neanderthal man to have been a fiction. In this context it is interesting to note that Engels,[58] in an essay written in 1876, came to the same basic conclusions as did Dart. From the fossil evidence, it is now accepted that the legs, hands and brains of modern man evolved in that order. Engels wrote: 'Presumably as an immediate consequence of their mode of life, which in climbing assigns different functions to the hands than to the feet, these apes when walking on level ground began to ... adopt a more and more erect gait. This was *the decisive step in the transition from ape to man*' (Engels's italics). He goes on to discuss the importance of the freeing of the hand and the gradual adaptations which enabled it to perform complex and delicate tasks. As he states, 'the decisive step had been taken: *the hand had become free* and could henceforth attain ever greater dexterity and skill'. After discussing the origin of language he concluded that labour and speech 'were the two most essential stimuli under the influence of which the brain of the ape gradually changed into that of man, which for all its similarity is far larger and more perfect'. Finally, Engels and Dart were agreed in the significance of the change to a carnivorous diet. 'Labour begins with the making of tools. And what are the most ancient tools that we find ... They are hunting and fishing implements, the former at the same time serving as weapons. But hunting and fishing presuppose the transition from an exclusively vegetable diet to the concomitant use of meat, and this is an important step in the process of transition from ape to man' (Engels). The important point here is not merely that Dart has been completely vindicated, but also that correct conclusions can often be reached by a recognition of basic principles.

The australopithecines are now known, from the structure of their pelvic girdles, to have stood as upright as modern man, although in all probability they ran rather than walked. A comparison of the girdles of the australopithecines with those of modern man and the apes shows quite clearly that they are man-like and not ape-like.[53] If the teeth are compared in the same way, the australopithecine dentition is seen to be essentially human, although it must be conceded that it is at the same time almost indistinguishable from the dentition of *Ramapithecus*. The main difference between the australopithecine dentition and that of modern man is one of size. The former is the more massive affair— hence the popular name of 'nutcracker-man' coined for one of Leakey's more recent finds.[116]

In contrast to these man-like features, the cranial capacity of the australopithecines was comparable with that of the modern apes, ranging from 300 to 600 cc., but despite this they had learnt to make a variety of implements from bones, teeth and horn—the 'osteodonto-keratic' culture of Dart.[52] The type of wear on these bones has been exactly simulated by Leakey, showing that these were used for digging, but, as Dart established, also as weapons.[51] He recorded some fifty baboon skulls from australopithecine sites all with a peculiar double depression in the bone, and he concluded that these had been caused by the long bones of antelopes wielded by the australopithecines. This particular thesis touched off a storm of controversy, and was vehemently denied by most leading authorities. It was argued that the majority of bone artifacts described by Dart were the remains of the activities of hyaenas; however, Ardrey has assembled evidence to demolish this particular argument. There seems little doubt that the australopithecines did use tools and weapons of bone. Moreover, Dart has further shown that the australopithecines sometimes met their end at the hands of their own kind.[51]

The australopithecines were not a homogeneous group; there were two distinct types which certainly differed in their respective ways of life. The more passive, heavily built form, *Australopithecus robustus*, had powerful jaws, and his teeth showed that he was mainly a vegetarian. He had heavy brow ridges and a marked sagittal crest for the insertion of the masticatory musculature (Fig. 45a–d). The other type, *A. africanus*, was more lightly built, with a more rounded head and a dentition that clearly indicated a diet with a fair proportion of meat in it (Fig. 45j–l). Such an ecological differentiation with the different effects on the teeth occurs at the present day with different tribes in the same region. It is a moot point whether these two co-existing populations of australo-pithecines should be placed in separate species. However, there seems every likelihood that the more pacific vegetarians did not survive competition with their more agile and aggressive brethren.

The later and most advanced of the australopithecines have created yet another great controversy which was argued in the columns of *Nature* from 1964 to 1966;[117,130] it concerns the so-called '*Homo habilis*' (Fig. 45e–g, m, n). In the first place, he had a cranial capacity of about 680 cc., the mandible was less robust than in typical australopithecines, the foot (unknown in other australopithecines) was similar to modern man's, the big toe was orientated in the same way and the foot was arched. *Homo habilis* stood about 4 ft. and could probably have walked much as we do. In the hand, the opposable thumb was comparatively short, but there is no doubt that he would have been easily capable of manufacturing stone implements. The flat terminal phalanges of the thumb and index finger indicate that he was adept at handling objects,

HOMO SAPIENS

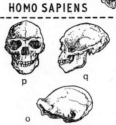

HOMO ERECTUS

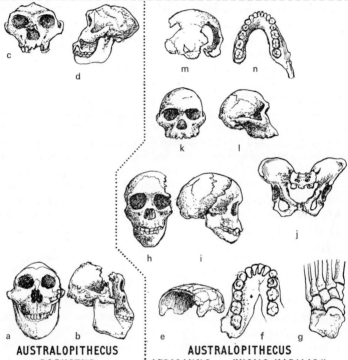

AUSTRALOPITHECUS ROBUSTUS

AUSTRALOPITHECUS AFRICANUS — "HOMO HABILIS"

FIG. 45. a–d. *Australopithecus robustus*: a, b. '*Zinjanthropus boisei*' from Olduvai, Bed I; c, d. '*Paranthropus robustus*' from Swartkrans; e–n. *Australopithecus africanus*; e–g. '*Homo habilis*': e. cranium, f. mandible, g. foot from Olduvai, Bed I; h–l. *A. africanus*: h, i. Taung skull; j. pelvic girdle from Sterkfontein; k, l. adult from Sterkfontein; m, n. '*Homo habilis*': m. cranium, n. mandible from Olduvai, Bed II; o–q. *Homo erectus*: o. Chellean man, Olduvai Bed II, p, q. '*Pithecanthropus*' from Peking; r–t. *Homo sapiens*: r. '*Homo neanderthalensis*' from La Chapelle-aux-Saints; s. Swanscombe man from Kent.

and clearly had an effective power-grip, but was still not capable of the fine work that requires a precision-grip—such as employed in wielding a pen.[129] Remains of this animal are found on living floors and with simple stone tools; they are also found near to remains of the *robustus* australopithecines. Large bones of ungulates cracked open for the marrow, as well as fish and small mammal remains, all provide evidence of hunting; and thus suggest that the *robustus* individual was the intruder on the site. The home, which the piles of stones show it to have been, must have been deserted at the time of the intrusion— leaving the dead of both groups behind—the adult intruder and the *habilis* child.

Leakey and his colleagues claimed that *Homo habilis* represented the true basic stock of humanity, with the australopithecines an aberrant side branch, and Leakey[118] himself has now (1966) gone so far as to suggest that it led direct to *Homo sapiens* and that *Homo erectus*—or the pithecanthropoids—was a side branch from the main stock just as the australopithecines were. There seems little doubt that in its structure this controversial form falls exactly between the australopithecines on the one hand and the more advanced *Homo erectus* on the other. Indeed Robinson[117] has noted that the early specimen of *H. habilis* falls within the range of the lightly built australopithecines, whilst the later one cannot be separated from *Homo erectus*. Indeed *H. habilis* provides a perfect link between two grades of human or hominid organisation. It is probably best to consider this new and important find as the most advanced of the australopithecines, or the most primitive of the pithecanthropoids or, following Robinson,[117] as both. The introduction of another new 'species' into the sequence seems to be quite unjustified. The morphological changes in this sequence are very minor; the main advances are cultural, that is behavioural.

Homo erectus—the First Religious Man

The pithecanthropoids, which are now included in the single species *Homo erectus*, bridge the gap between modern man and the australopithecines (Fig. 45, o–q).[87] Their hind limbs are indistinguishable from those of modern man, and hence it is clear that their gait and posture were identical to our own. This species is found in Africa and also in Asia, in China and Indonesia, and recently has been recorded from Hungary. The cranial capacity ranges from about 775 to 1100 cc., and so overlaps the lower range of our own species. The cranial vault is inflated, but strong brow ridges are still present. The face is reduced and approaches more that of modern man, and the dentition is essentially that of *H. sapiens*. Although most pithecanthropoids were chinless, some forms show the incipient development of a chin. But perhaps one of the significant advances made by this group was their discovery of the use of fire. They also manufactured simple stone implements such as axes and scrapers, but do not seem to have evolved the precision-grip. However, the most sophisticated aspect of their behaviour was the fact that they appear to have indulged in cannibalism. This may not have been merely a question of food, of which, from the evidence of their middens, they had sufficient, but may have been part of a system of beliefs. It seems reasonable to postulate that the purpose of this particular activity was to acquire some of the qualities of the victim; by ingesting part of the honoured person one would hope to acquire some of his spiritual values. This same pattern appears to have survived in one extant religion, which has as its centrepiece the spring fertility ritual of human sacrifice of the god-king and his resurrection three days later;[17,64,77,165] in this same religion ritual cannibalism survives where symbolic flesh and blood of the human sacrifice are eaten and drunk (biscuits and wine taking the place of actual flesh and blood).[228] The role of 'religion' in the life of early man was clear. It provided the framework of a code of behaviour in the community, but, to be effective, it had to be seen to be based on powers beyond those of mankind, and these were the spirits which controlled the sequence of the seasons. A system of beliefs built on this foundation would be viable through many generations since it would not rely on the changing fortunes of particular leaders. Although there is no way of determining exactly how advanced the beliefs of *Homo erectus* were, there can be little doubt that he was 'religious' to some degree.

Homo sapiens, including Neanderthal Man

From this stage of development it is but a short step to *Homo sapiens*. The earliest recognisable modern man is Swanscombe from about 250 thousand years ago (Fig. 45s), but a later racial type evolved which, although now included in the species *H. sapiens*, was formerly given the status of an independent species namely *H. neanderthalensis*. This form, with its heavy brow ridges and prognathous chinless face (Fig. 45r) has caused a great deal of confusion; as Cave[32] pointed out, neanderthal man is popularly depicted as 'imperfectly erect of stance, bent-kneed, flat-footed and in-toed, with a convex back continued uninterruptedly into an equally convex 'bull-kneck', a head thrust forward of the spine, a lower limb incapable of full extension, and as progressing by a clumsy, shuffling gait upon the outer borders of his feet'. This picture, based essentially on the La Chapelle-aux-Saints skeleton, contrasts with the type of posture and gait that was present even in the australopithecines and, if true, would represent a reversion to a more ape-like posture—a state difficult of explanation, since this degenerate brutish man with, let it be remembered, a greater cranial capacity than many modern men, was exceedingly successful for a good many thousand years. Of course this interpretation agreed with what was expected of primitive man in the first few decades of the present century; today, like Piltdown man, it appears quite anomalous. Cave[32] re-examined the skeleton on which all the restorations had been based, and one can do no better than quote his results.

The skull is possibly, the atlas certainly, ill-restored. Anatomical study of some important points is precluded by the absence, or the imperfection, of skeletal components. The backbone, particularly in its cervical portion, is so distorted by severe and generalised osteoarthritis as to exclude any reliable estimation of its original curvatures. The posturally important upper cervical vertebrae are pathological in the extreme: the diseased odontoid is deflected; the atlas and axis no longer articulate naturally; the fifth, sixth and seventh cervicals are disease-distorted in bodies and zygopophyses; the upper cervical discs must have atrophied to disappearance long before death. The thoracic and lumbar vertebrae show marked arthritic change and body-height decrease, due to age and disc shrinkage. The severity and extent of the osteoarthritis deformans present renders suspect, to say the least, the Boule interpretation of spinal posture.

The admitted length, non-bifidity and anteversion of the cervical spinous processes are not 'simian' traits, as alleged, but features falling within the range of variation encountered in modern Europeans.

The characters of the sacro-pelvic fragments are obviously indicative of a truly upright body posture. The degree of curvature of the femoral shaft and the degree of retroversion of the tibial head fall within the known range of variation in modern races: there is no morphological justification for the concept of a permanently semi-flexed knee-joint. Tibial torsion is positive (as in modern man), not negative (as in apes); hence the foot, in many respects 'ultramodern', directed its toes outwards and was designed to subserve a true bipedal orthograde posture.

Without multiplying details it may be affirmed that the La Chapelle skeleton admits of a reconstruction radically different from Boule's, one which, while not denying distinctive neanderthal morphology, proclaims this individual to have stood and walked as does modern man.

As well as being severely diseased this skeleton is of an old man, aged between 60 and 70 years—at a time when, as Calvin Wells[243] has noted, 'only one in twenty lived beyond the age of forty; eighty per cent perished before they were thirty'. This old man had obviously been carefully tended by his tribe, the style with which he was buried being a further indication of his standing. Indeed, from the manner of burial, one has the impression that there was a belief in an after-life or at least in the immortality of the spirit.

The relationship between neanderthal man and modern man presents a number of problems, since both races appear to have migrated over large distances and invaded each other's territories, although it seems likely that for much of their history they were isolated from one another. Wickler[250] has suggested that modern man evolved in the Western World and the neanderthals originated in eastern Asia. During the third interglacial the neanderthals spread into the Middle East. In the fourth Ice Age modern-type man retreated south, and his position in Europe was taken by a further invasion of so-called classic neanderthals; these men were sturdy and of small stature and were clearly adapted to life in a cold climate. It is an odd fact that the taurodont molars which are a feature of neanderthal man are now found only in the eskimos.

During a warm spell in the fourth Ice Age modern man, in the form of Cro-Magnon man, swept into the regions inhabited by the neanderthals, and in a very short space of time completely replaced them. The cultural traditions established by the neanderthals appear to have been continued and further developed. The variety of stone tools was greatly increased; the burial of the dead was a more elaborate affair. Hunters were buried with the tools of their trade, children with their ornaments. Probably the most familiar innovation was 'Art'— for some people this truly distinguishes mankind. However, art with a capital 'A' is really something that made its appearance only during the last few centuries. Certainly there were unlikely to have been many leisure pursuits during the Stone Age; art had a function in society. By portraying an animal, or an enemy for that matter, one was capturing part of its spirit; and if it were transfixed by a weapon, albeit a spiritual one, the prey unbeknown to itself was severely handicapped. With this foreknowledge the confidence, and hence success, of the hunters was greatly augmented. Similarly the carving of Venuses for fertility purposes must have been a great help to the people concerned. Indeed pudendal graffiti appear to have continued down through the ages with little change, and such portrayals must, if only by virtue of their antiquity, have attained a certain degree of respectability. The four Venuses of Angles-sur-L'Anglin (Fig. 46) would seem to have survived in the Nordic Runes for birth and as the tree of life symbol, which when reversed becomes the symbol for death, and at the present time it continues to be utilised in many spheres of modern society, the

Nuclear Disarmament badge is derived from this symbol and the combination of both runes with the centre link forming the stem of the letter P survives as a Christian emblem.[223]

In spite of the appearance of man the artist, survival depended on hunting, later herding. The prey was domesticated. This last development set the scene for what is termed the Neolithic Revolution. Gordon Childe[34] has emphasised the significance of the establishment

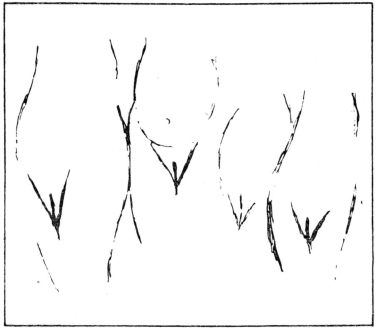

FIG. 46. Palaeolithic cave carvings of Venuses from Angles-sur-l'Anglin, Vienne, France. (from Halstead Tarlo, by permission of Editors of *Penthouse*).

of settled food-producing communities, the domestication of animals and plants, and the development of such crafts as pottery for domestic utensils. From excavations in Jericho it is evident that such settled communities were first established some ten thousand years ago. Thereafter they spread over many regions of the earth, although there is now evidence that this cultural stage was achieved independently at different times by widely separated communities.[40]

The Neolithic Revolution marks the beginning of human civilisation. The tilling of the land and the settling of permanent living sites resulted

N

in a vast increase in the types of work done by man and woman—
specialised tasks were performed and for these special skills were
required. The labour of men became characterised by specialisation,
hunters, tillers of the soil, potters, millers, weavers, and travelling
salesmen. Each man had his allotted place in society and, although no
one individual was ever indispensable, society's success was a function
of the integration of the multitudinous activities of its members. The
development of crafts and trade led eventually to the growth of
townships, and as with the australopithecines the more pastoral the
life, the less vigorous and aggressive. Again there is the situation where
a major advance, which at one period is in the long run a regression
from an earlier state, nevertheless has within it the seeds of still further
advance. The spread of settled agricultural communities would simply
have led mankind into a backwater of evolution such as that in which
the pacific apes, the gorillas and chimpanzees, now find themselves.
The vigour of competition in the towns prevented this, and perhaps
the basic antipathy between town and country stems from this.
However, in contrast to the situation with the australopithecines, both
town and country dwellers were mutually dependent upon one another,
and consequently a *modus vivendi* was established. The conservatism of
the countryman and the radicalism of the town dweller have been
recognised through the ages, and nowhere is this more evident than
where there are advanced industrial communities. However, the history
of civilisation has neither been simply a story of the conflict between
town and country nor a record of increasing technological advance.
Rather it has been an unending catalogue of wars, with emphasis on
the improvement of the instruments of war. It is no mere coincidence
that the most advanced and powerful nations at the present time are
those which devote a considerable proportion of their wealth towards
the accummulation and perfection of the weapons of war.

A Definition of Man

In the gradual transition from *Ramapithecus* to our modern
civilisation mankind originated somewhere along the line. Since we
look upon ourselves as a rather special species and fundamentally
different from all other living things—a peculiar arrogance on our
part—much effort is consequently spent on the intellectual exercise of
defining Man. As with so many classifications, this must inevitably
mean the drawing of a completely arbitrary boundary at the point
where, it is believed, no other organism could cross over. We have seen
this situation before, in the choice of criteria to separate the mammals
from the reptiles. Such boundaries are artificial, and even when they

appear to be satisfactory, it should always be remembered that they are drawn across what is in reality a continuum of change. In life there are no hard and fast boundaries, only imperceptible gradations. This having been said, there is, nevertheless, a certain satisfaction in being able to define our own kind. As can be expected, there is no diagnosis that will be agreed by all. One definition simply states that man achieves the human state at the point when he is given a soul. This is the sort of event that is remarkably difficult to pin down in the fossil record. The crux of this matter is the recognition of spiritual values; this implies a high level of conceptual thought coupled with the idea of the dichotomy between body and mind or spirit or soul. This dichotomy is the consequence of the recognition of qualities which, although emanating from physical beings, are nonetheless intangible. From this it is but a short step to the concept that these spiritual values can have an existence of their own, even though they may be housed in a human frame. The belief that it is possible to acquire these intangible qualities by consuming those people who clearly possess them, is common to many societies and religions. It can thus be inferred that peoples who indulge in ritual cannibalism must have some concept of the human soul, and if one chooses the acquisition of a soul to be the criterion for one's definition of man, I think one can safely suggest that this must be at the point where man himself is aware of such things. From this it would follow that *Homo erectus* falls into the category of the first man.

A further criterion that is popularly used is the appearance of art, the point at which man is supposed to have expended his creative activity in producing works of beauty, i.e. when man first developed an aesthetic sense. There is no doubt that the cave paintings have a vigour and grace seldom found in the work of contemporary painters. This, however, is simply because they were portraying living things in which the whole pattern of bone and muscle produces a functioning whole that has a unity that does not jar the senses. However, the fact that we look at art today in the way we do, does not allow us to assume that ancient man had the same attitude of mind. There is ample evidence that he did not. His paintings were executed in the deepest and darkest of caves; these were no picture galleries for those with a penchant for things of beauty. These paintings were a serious and important part of life in the hunting community; moreover, they show that man believed in spirits and also in their partial control by direct representation. The profusion of religious paintings throughout history would seem to bear this out. Basically art was a further reflection of the religious nature of primitive man. If one wishes art to be the dividing line between man and non-man then Cro-Magnon man must be the first man.

Both the criteria of 'soul' and 'art' are manifestations of man's ability to think abstract thoughts; indeed conceptual thought is perhaps the real hall-mark of mankind. It is known that the higher non-human primates can and do use tools; which implies an exceedingly high degree of intelligence. Thus, man is generally defined not so much as a tool user but more as a tool maker, 'Man the tool-maker'.[136] The ability to fashion natural objects to perform future tasks must mean the ability to think ahead, to plan for future contingencies. Such a being is clearly capable, to a certain extent, of conceptual thought and could perhaps be classified as man. There is, in fact, something almost noble in the idea of man's advance being a factor of his craftsmanship, the human state being reached through the fashioning of tools. This pleasing notion has been somewhat upset by the observations of Dr. Jane Goodall.[69] From her observations of chimpanzees in the wild, as opposed to those in captivity, she was able to prove that these primates modified natural objects for such purposes as obtaining food and water that would otherwise have been unattainable. By definition these animals were tool-makers, albeit of the *ad hoc* variety. Unless they were to be included as fellow-men, the definition of man the tool-maker would have to go.

However, the problem is not an insuperable one. It is really a question of the tools. Engels[58] noted that man's first tools were for hunting, and Ardrey[18] has stressed the fact that 'tool' is really a euphemism for 'weapon'. In fact, as Ardrey has cogently argued, man's ancestry can be traced to a line of higher primates that deserted life in the trees and took to open country, but the key feature of the line that led to man was that it consisted of group hunting predators. Not only were the australopithecines carnivores and predators, but they also wielded weapons. Later their descendants learned the art of fashioning weapons. The superior effectiveness of stone implements over that of bone clubs would have given the wielders of the former mastery over the users of the latter. Indeed one of the major developments of mankind has been the continuing perfection of his means of killing. It is clearly comforting to think of man the tool-maker, since the development of peaceful crafts is clearly implied. But early man and his precursors were not pacific craftsmen, they were killers. It is this trait to which we owe our success through the ages. Man's unique contribution to evolution, which distinguishes him from his fellow creatures, is that he makes weapons for future use!

17 : The Future of Man

After surveying the pattern of vertebrate evolution from its earliest beginnings up to and including ourselves, the normal reaction is to question whether anything of this story is of relevance to the present and also whether it can give any clue as to what is likely to happen in the future. The population explosion and the inadequacy of food resources to meet it, which bulk so largely in current thinking about the future, do not present any problem in the overall perspective of human evolution. Were this current problem to become acute, famine and wars are likely, in the first instance, to act as the most effective controls. In view of the prodigious waste of foodstuffs in the United States and Europe, and the industries devoted to pet-foods, it is hard to visualise the problem of over-population as a global one. In essence, advances in medical science have run ahead of agricultural techniques and the latter ahead of education, so that the birth rate is in excess of the death rate. Agriculture is catching up; only education lags far behind. It can be confidently expected that these three aspects of human progress, now out of phase, will eventually become integrated. The real problem is a short term one; for at the moment there is no need for any human being to starve to death. It is a question of the distribution of resources; but no Western community is prepared to forgo any of the luxuries it enjoys in order that the less well endowed should survive. Here too technological evolution is far in advance of social.

In the context of geological time the population explosion crisis is temporary and should be quickly brought under control. Other aspects of the human state present much longer term problems, and would seem to be best understood as consequences which follow naturally from group hunting predation. They also reveal a number of conflicting trends in society; again the origins of these can be traced back to our former existence as group hunting predators.

Perhaps one of the most striking features of man is the apparent difference between the way people act as individuals and the way they act in a crowd. This is frequently remarked upon even in the popular press: 'When people go to a football match, they seem to lose their identity and to become part of a sinister elemental force. And when that force is compounded with chauvinism, the result is peculiarly menacing—not unlike Hitler's Nuremberg rallies' (Grigg, in the *Guardian*, 28.7.1966). In recent times there have been numerous examples of mass hysteria, ranging from lynch mobs and race riots to the grotesque manifestations of the Nazis and the witch-hunting McCarthy era in the United States. But this has always been the way; one has only to think of the innumerable religious wars in which no quarter was given on either side, the almost infinite catalogue of mass murder and genocide throughout human history. In all these events there was always an enemy, either real or imagined; with the Nazis it was the Jews, with the Americans today it is the Communists. Yet this same phenomenon when acted out on a different stage gives us an equal catalogue of the noblest acts of man, the heroism and self-sacrifice that are called forth when communities face terrible dangers whether from marauding invaders or natural catastrophes such as floods. Sargant has described the mechanism of engendering mass hysteria whether in evangelical meetings or in political rallies. He has amply demonstrated that the human brain can be worked on, so that the individual can be subjugated to something not only outside of himself but even to something that was previously entirely alien, by the technique of brain-washing employed by the early Methodists and by the Communists. This can be used for good or ill, but whosoever employs these techniques of religious or political conversion always does it in the sincere belief that it is for the good of all concerned. Herein lies its inherent danger: in the name of some chosen ideology the greatest and noblest acts are committed, but so are the most hideous.

Since this behavioural pattern runs through all human communities, even if only in the intense partisanship of football supporters, it would seem obvious that it is a fundamental trait common to our species. This being so, it must have had some important biological advantage for our forebears. Here we return to our group hunting predators. For a society of animals that as individuals are puny, survival, let alone success, is possible only if they act in concert. For particular activities such as hunting, defence, or attack, the needs of the individual must be subordinated to the good of all. This is seen in the self-sacrifice of baboons in the defence of their communities, so movingly described by Ardrey. Without this built-in type of behaviour no such communities could hope to be viable. This group activity is directed against the enemies of the society, and these are often simply possible territorial rivals.[19,123] Unfortunately, our group hunting inheritance is such that there will always be a need for this particular trait to find expression.[31] It would be pleasant to imagine that sporting competitions would serve this purpose, but it seems far more likely that man will always find some pretext to 'justify' making war on his neighbours in one way or another.

So far, I have discussed the aggressive group personality of man, but this aggressiveness does not arise of its own accord. There has always to be a rabble rouser, an orator, a prophet, a leader; in all social animals there is a hierarchy or pecking order. This implies differences in personality, and, as in Pavlov's dogs, there are certain basic personality traits common to both species—dog and man; and within these there are also different levels of ability. In natural communities animals find their proper level in society; only in the non-human world do true meritocracies exist. It is vital in such communities that every individual produces the maximum of what he or she is capable. Human societies are also stratified; all are class societies. They differ from those of other social animals in that the stratifications are more rigid and the greater part of human potential ability is wasted. The pathway to the professions in this country is confined in the main to the middle classes. The proportion of children from working class backgrounds that pass through the higher echelons of the educational system is comparatively small. Exactly the same pertains in the Soviet Union, where the Universities in the main draw their students from families with some sort of academic background—the middle class, in fact. The present system of educational streaming in this country accentuates this condition, although the introduction of comprehensive education may go some way to prevent such waste of human resources. Children from the more academic backgrounds will still retain the advantage over children of comparable ability from different backgrounds. In time there may be a freeway in society that will give children equality of opportunity, but perhaps this is a forlorn hope, since there is a drive on the part of the parents to ensure that the gains they made should be handed on to their offspring. There is always likely to be a tendency for a class system to become ultimately more, rather than less, rigid.

As well as this horizontal stratification of society there is a vertical one, and the character of this may determine the fate of the society concerned. This vertical division is between male and female. The most obvious distinction is the physical sexual dimorphism, but the behavioural patterns also differ. In general terms these differences are well known: women favour security and stability; men tend to prefer adventure and change. This is borne out even in politics, where men in the main vote for radical parties, women for conservative.

The really fundamental differences of attitude are revealed in the woman's preference for the known, for retaining the *status quo*, for conformity, in contrast with the man's for the unknown, for change—except when running with the crowd. From these two basic attitudes all the rest flow. Again these differences seem to have been a common feature throughout history, the women sitting at home and the men going off to seek adventure, generally in wars. These differences also would appear to be a further consequence of our group hunting past. The main hunting would be carried out by the males of the group, who would be distinct individuals with different gifts; in fact the group would be highly varied as far as their individual personalities were concerned, but, when required, these differences would be sunk for the sake of the common endeavour. The females would stay back in the camp to bear and bring up their offspring. Their prime need would be for security and stability.

It is the basic incompatibility of the requirements of the two sexes that makes their mutual relationships interesting, for it is a conflict that in the nature of things can never be resolved. Indeed looking back over the history of the vertebrates, it is a microcosm of the basic conflict that the fossil record reveals again and again. The more closely an animal conforms to its surroundings, and the more adapted it becomes to a particular environment, the more successful it appears to be for a time. But the more perfect the fit to the environment, the more certain is extinction. Time after time it is the unspecialised forms, remaining highly variable and adaptable, that survive. The main tendency is to join the current rat-race, yet it is on those that opt out—the apparent failures—that the future frequently seems to depend.

If we look at contemporary society in such advanced countries as the United States, the Soviet Union and Britain, we find that the one factor they have in common is the increasing tendency for people to conform more and more rigidly to the social standards of society.

The unorthodox is tolerated less and less, people simply do not like to be different, and life is more comfortable if the norms of accepted behaviour are adhered to. Such is the nature of conformism in North America—admittedly a matriarchal society—that Nursall,[135] in discussing what mankind will be like in a mere thousand years from now, wrote: 'He will be socially well-orientated and probably will not readily suffer non-conformity. His problems and pleasures will all be artificial, and he will look back on us with pity, as we look ahead to him with dismay'. This daunting prospect is simply the logical result of the extrapolation of current trends into the future. There is little doubt that, once the unorthodox is no longer tolerated, then society loses its vitality. Unless a society can maintain variety, it will go the way of Nursall's prediction. From the present showing it seems that the advanced societies of today are heading strongly in this direction.

But we have seen all this before. Successful communities get ever more successful and ever more specialised, they become 'socially well-orientated', and then they are taken by surprise. Primitive communities suddenly sweep the board, the embolomeres—a backwater in the main stream of labyrinthodont evolution—the semiaquatic archosaurs during the radiation of the paramammals, the woodland birds during the heyday of the pterosaurs, the arboreal primates during the explosive evolution of the modern mammals, and, to come to the present century, the backward peasant society of Russia that emerged as one of the world's greatest powers. Even nearer to the present day, the emergence of China as a world power has come so suddenly that the United States still cannot quite believe it. History seems to stress the identical lesson of the fossil record: the most advanced communities do not give rise to still further advanced communities, they become complacent instead; affluence saps their evolutionary vitality.

If the pattern of vertebrate evolution continues as it has in the past, and there is no reason to suppose that it will not, then one is forced to conclude that the great powers of the world today will be replaced by others with more vitality. Looking at the world scene from a palaeontologist's point of view, one would expect that the great civilisation of the future would arise from the present turmoil in Africa. Here, more than anywhere else in the world, is a region seething with violence and vitality. Here, if anywhere, the future of man must lie. The keynote of advance is variety, and here it is in such profusion as to verge on anarchy.

The lesson of five hundred million years of vertebrate history is that to be perfectly adapted to your environment ultimately spells disaster. This is fittingly crystallised by de Beer in a phrase as appropriate to modern society as it is to the overall perspective of vertebrate evolution: 'the paths of adaptive glory lead but to the grave of extinction'.

References

GENERAL

1. BYSTROW, A. P. 1957. *Man in the Past, Present and Future.* Leningrad.
2. GOODRICH, E. S. 1930. *Studies on the Structure and Development of Vertebrates.* Constable & Co., London. (1958 Reprint. Dover Publications, New York.)
3. GREGORY, W. K. 1951. *Evolution Emerging.* Macmillan, New York.
4. HARLAND, W. B., *et al.* (eds.). 1967. *The Fossil Record.* Geological Society, London.
5. HUENE, F. VON. 1956. *Paläontologie und Phylogenie der Niederen Tetrapoden.* Gustav Fischer Verlag, Jena.
6. JARVIK, E. 1960. *Théories de l'Évolution des Vertébrés.* Masson et Cie, Paris.
7. KERKUT, G. A. 1960. *Implications of Evolution.* Pergamon Press, Oxford.
8. LEHMAN, J. P. 1959. *L'Évolution des Vertébrés inférieures. Quelques problèmes.* Dunod, Paris.
9. ORLOV, J. (ed.) 1964. *Fundamentals of Palaeontology (Osnovy Paleontologii).* Moscow.
    11. Agnathans, Fish. (OBRUCHEV, D., ed.).
    12. Amphibians, Reptiles and Birds. (ROZDESTVENSKI, A. K. and TATARINOV, L. P., eds.).
    13. Mammals. (GROMOVA, V. I., ed.).
10. ROMER, A. S. 1949. *The Vertebrate Body.* W. B. Saunders Co., Philadelphia, London.
11. — 1956. *Osteology of the Reptiles.* Univ. Chicago Press, Chicago.
12. — 1966. *Vertebrate Paleontology.* (3rd. Ed.). Univ. Chicago Press, Chicago.
13. SMITH, H. M. 1960. *Evolution of Chordate Structure. An Introduction to Comparative Anatomy.* Holt, Rinehart & Winston, Inc.
14. WATSON, D. M. S. 1951. *Paleontology and Modern Biology.* Yale Univ. Press, New Haven.
15. YOUNG, J. Z. 1957. *The Life of Mammals.* Clarendon Press, Oxford.
16. — 1962. *The Life of Vertebrates.* (2nd ed.). Clarendon Press, Oxford.

SPECIAL

17. ALLEN, G. 1931. *The Evolution of the Idea of God.* Watts, London.
18. ARDREY, R. 1961. *African Genesis.* Collins, London.
19. — 1967. *The Territorial Imperative.* Collins, London.

191

20. BAIRD, D. and CARROLL, R. L. 1967. Romeriscus, the oldest known reptile. *Science*, **157**: 56–9.

21. BARRINGTON, E. J. W. 1965. *The Biology of Hemichordata and Protochordata*. Oliver and Boyd, Edinburgh.

22. BERRILL, N. J. 1955. *The Origin of the Vertebrates*. Clarendon Press, Oxford.

23. BONAPARTE, J. F. 1967. New vertebrate evidence for a southern transatlantic connexion during the Lower or Middle Triassic. *Palaeontology*, **10**: 554–63.

24. BONE, Q. 1960. The origin of the chordates. *J. Linn. Soc. (Zool.)* **44**: 252–69.

25. — 1963. The central nervous system. In *The Biology of Myxine*. (BRODAL, A. and FÄNGE, R., eds.). Universitetsforlaget, Oslo.

26. BROOKES, R. 1763. *The Natural History of Waters, Earths, Stones, Fossils, and Minerals, with their Virtues, Properties, and Medicinal Uses: To which is added, The method in which LINNAEUS has treated these subjects*. Vol. V. London.

27. BROUGH, M. C. and BROUGH, J. 1967. Studies in early tetrapods. I. The Lower Carboniferous Microsaurs. II. *Microbrachius*, the type microsaur. III. The genus *Gephyrostegus*. *Phil. Trans. R. Soc.*, B, **252**: 107–65.

28. BYSTROW, A. P. 1955. The microstructure of the dermal armour of the jawless vertebrates from the Silurian and Devonian. *Acad. Sci. USSR. Berg Mem. Vol.*, 472–523.

29. CAMPBELL, B. G. 1967. *Human Evolution. An Introduction to Man's Adaptations*. Heinemann, London.

30. CARROLL, R. L. 1964. The earliest reptiles. *J. Linn. Soc. (Zool.)*, **45**: 61–83.

31. CARTHY, J. D. and EBLING, F. J. (eds.). 1964. *The Natural History of Aggression*. Academic Press, London and New York.

32. CAVE, A. J. E. 1959. Posture of Neanderthal man. *Proc. XVth Int. Congr. Zool.*: 431–2.

33. CHARIG, A. J. 1966. Stance and gait in the archosaur reptiles. *Advmt Sci., Lond.*, **22**: 537 (Abstr.).

34. CHILDE, V. G. 1936. *Man Makes Himself*. Watts, London.

35. CLARK, W. E. LE GROS. 1965. *History of the Primates*. British Museum (Natural History), London.

36. COLBERT, E. H. 1951. *The Dinosaur Book. The ruling reptiles and their relatives*. McGraw-Hill, New York.

37. — 1962. *Dinosaurs. Their discovery and their world*. Hutchinson, London.

38. — 1965. *The Age of Reptiles*. Weidenfeld & Nicolson, London.

39. — 1966. A gliding reptile from the Triassic of New Jersey. *Am. Mus. Novit.*, **2246**: 1–23.

40. COLE, S. 1965. *The Neolithic Revolution*. British Museum (Natural History), London.

41. COX, C. B. 1967. Cutaneous respiration and the origin of the modern Amphibia. *Proc. Linn. Soc. Lond.*, **178**: 37–47.

42. CROMPTON, A. W. 1958. The cranial morphology of a new genus and species of ictidosaurian. *Proc. zool. Soc. Lond.*, **130**: 183–216.

43. — 1963. The evolution of the mammalian jaw. *Evolution*, **17**, 431–439.

44. — 1963. On the lower jaw of *Diarthrognathus* and the origin of the mammalian lower jaw. *Proc. zool. Soc. Lond.*, **140**: 697–753.

45. CROMPTON, A. W. and CHARIG, A. J. 1962. A new ornithischian from the Upper Triassic of South Africa. *Nature, Lond.*, **196**: 1074–7.

46. CUPPY, W. 1964. *How to Become Extinct*. Dover Publications, New York.

47. CURREY, J. D. 1960. Differences in the blood-supply of bone of different histological types. *Q. Jl. Microsc. Sci.*, **101**: 351–70.

48. — 1962. Strength of bone. *Nature, Lond.*, **195**: 513–4.

49. — 1964. Three anologies to explain the mechanical properties of bone. *Biorheol.*, **2**: 1–10.

50. DART, R. A. 1925. Australopithecus africanus: the man-ape of South Africa. *Nature, Lond.*, **115**: 195–9.

51. — 1953. The Predatory Transition from Ape to Man. *Int. anthrop. ling. Rev.*, **1**: (4), 201–19.

52. — 1957. The Osteodontokeratic Culture of Australopithecus Prometheus. *Transv. Mus. Mem.*, **10**.

53. DAY, M. H. 1965. *Guide to Fossil Man. A Handbook of Human Palaeontology*. Cassell, London.

54. DENISON, R. H. 1941. The soft anatomy of Bothriolepis. *J. Paleont.*, **15**: 535–61.

55. — 1956. A review of the habitat of the earliest vertebrates. *Fieldiana, Geol.*, **11**: 359–457.

56. — 1963. The early history of the vertebrate calcified skeleton. *Clin. Orthop.*, **31**: 141–52.

57. EDMUND, G. 1960. Tooth replacement phenomena in the lower vertebrates. *Contr. Life Sci. Div., Ont. Mus.*, **52**: 1–190.

58. ENGELS, F. 1876. *The part played by labour in the transition from ape to man*. Foreign Languages Publ. Hse., Moscow. (1952).

59. FAHLBUSCH, K. 1964. Die Stellung der Conodontida im biologischen System. *Palaeontographica*, A, **123**: 137–201.

60. FIENNES, R. 1965. Man's role in the evolution of the dog. *New Scient.*, **25**: 84–6.

61. FISHER, J. 1967. The radiation of birds. In *The Fossil Record* (HARLAND, W. B. *et al.*, eds.). Geological Society, London.

62. FONTAINE, M., DAMAS, H., ROCHON-DUVIGNEAUD, A. and PASTEELS, J. 1958. Classe des Cyclostomes. Formes actuels: Super-Ordre des Petromyzonoidea et des Myxinoidea. In *Traité de Zoologie* (GRASSE, P. P., ed.), **13**(1): 15–172. Masson et Cie. Paris.

63. FOX, H. 1959. A study of the development of the head and pharynx of the larval urodele *Hynobius* and its bearing on the evolution of the vertebrate head. *Phil. Trans. R. Soc.*, B., **242**: 151–205.

64. FRAZER, J. G. 1922. *The Golden Bough: a study in magic and religion*. Macmillan & Co., London.

65. FROST, H. M. 1960. Introduction to joint biomechanics. *Henry Ford Hosp. med. Bull.*, **8**: 415–32.

66. GARDEN, R. S. 1961. The structure and function of the proximal end of the femur. *J. Bone Jnt Surg.*, **43B**: 576–89.

67. GARSTANG, W. 1928. The morphology of the Tunicata, and its bearings on the phylogeny of the Chordata. *Q. J. microsc. Sci.*, **71**: 51–187.

68. — 1951. *Larval Forms and other zoological verses.* Blackwell's, Oxford.

69. GOODALL, J. 1964. Tool-using and aimed throwing in a community of free-living chimpanzees. *Nature, Lond.*, **201**: 1264–6.

70. GOODRICH, E. S. 1916. Classification of the Reptilia. *Proc. R. Soc. B.*, **89**: 261–76.

71. GRIFFITHS, I. 1963. The phylogeny of the Salientia. *Biol. Rev.*, **38**: 241–92.

72. GROSS, W. 1930. Die Fische des mittleren Old Red Sud-Livland. *Geol. Paläont. Abh.* N.F., **18**: 121–56.

HALSTEAD, L. B. (see under TARLO)

73. HAM, A. W. and LEESON, T. S. 1965. *Histology* (5th ed.). Lippincott Co., Philadelphia.

74. HANKIN, E. H. and WATSON, D. M. S. 1914. On the flight of pterodactyls. *Aeronaut. J.*, **1914**: 324–35.

75. HARDY, A. C. 1954. Escape from specialisation. In *Evolution as a process.* (HUXLEY, J., HARDY, A. C. and FORD, E. B., eds.). Allen and Unwin, London.

76. HAUGHTON, S. H. 1956. Gondwanaland and the distribution of early reptiles. *Geol. Soc. S. Afr.*, **56** (Annex): 1–30.

77. HAWTON, H. 1950. *The Thinker's Handbook. A Guide to Religious Controversy.* Rationalist Press Association, London.

78. HEINTZ, A. 1939. Cephalaspida from Downtonian of Norway. *Skr. norske Vidensk-Akad.*, 1. Mat.-Naturv. Kl., **5**: 1–119.

79. HIIEMÄE, K. M. S. 1967. Masticatory function in the mammals. *J. dent. Res.*, **46**: 883–93.

80. — 1968. The mammalian dentition and its functional variations. *Roy. dent. Hosp. Mag.* In the press.

81. HILDEBRAND, M. 1960. How animals run. *Scient. Am.*, **202**: (5), 148–57.

82. HOFFSTETTER, R. 1962. Revue des recentes acquisitions concernant l'histoire et la systematique des Squamates. In *Problèmes actuels de Paléontologie (Évolution des Vertébrés)*; *Colloques int. Cent. natn. Rech. scient.*, **104**: 243–79.

83. HOLMGREN, N. 1942. Studies on the head of fishes. An embryological, morphological and phylogenetical study. Pt. 3. The phylogeny of elasmobranch fishes. *Acta zool.*, **23**: 129–261.

84. HOPSON, J. A. 1966. The origin of the mammalian middle ear. *Am. Zoologist*, **6**: 437–50.

85. — 1964. Tooth replacement in cynodont, dicynodont and therocephalian reptiles. *Proc. zool. Soc. Lond.*, **142**: 625–54.

86. HOWELL, F. C. 1966. *Early Man.* Time-Life International, Amsterdam.

87. HOWELLS, W. W. 1966. Homo erectus. *Scient. Am.*, **215**(5): 46–53.

88. IVANOV, A. V. 1963. *Pogonophora.* Academic Press, London and New York.

89. JAMES, W. W. 1957. A further study of dentine. *Trans. zool. Soc. Lond.*, 29: 1–66.

90. JARVIK, E. 1942. On the structure of the snout of crossopterygians and lower gnathostomes in general. *Zool. Bidr. Uppsala*, 21: 235–675.

91. — 1955. The oldest tetrapods and their forerunners. *Scient. Mon.*, N.Y., 80: 141–54.

92. — 1959. Dermal fin-rays and Holmgren's Principle of Delamination. *K. svenska VetenskAkad. Handl.* 6(1): 1–51.

93. — 1963. The composition of the intermandibular division of the head in fish and tetrapods and the diphyletic origin of the tetrapod tongue. *K. svenska VetenskAkad. Handl.*, 9(1): 1–74.

94. — 1963. The Fossil Vertebrates from East Greenland and their Zoological Importance. *Experientia*, 19: 284–9.

95. — 1965. Specializations in early vertebrates. *Annls. Soc. roy. zool. Belg.*, 94: 11–95.

96. — 1965. On the origin of girdles and paired fins. *Israel Jnl. Zool.*, 14: 141–72.

97. — 1966. Remarks on the structure of the snout in *Megalichthys* and certain other rhipidistid crossopterygians. *Ark. Zool.*, 19: 41–98.

98. JEPSEN, G. L. 1964. Riddles of the terrible lizards. *Am. Scient.*, 52: 227–46. (Also: Terrible lizards revisited. *Princeton Alumni Weekly*, 44: (10), 6–10, 17–19).

99. KAUFFMAN, E. G. and KESLING, R. V. 1960. An Upper Cretaceous ammonite bitten by a mosasaur. *Contr. Mus. Paleont. Univ. Mich.*, L5: 193–248.

100. KELLOGG, R. 1936. A review of the Archaeoceti. *Publs Carnegie Instn*, 482: 1–366.

101. KERMACK, K. A. 1951. A note on the habits of sauropods. *Ann. Mag. nat. Hist.* Ser. 12, 4: 830–2.

102. — 1965. The origin of mammals. *Science Jl.* 1(7): 66–72.

103. KERMACK, K. A. and MUSSETT, F. 1958. The jaw articulation of the Docodonta and the classification of Mesozoic mammals. *Proc. R. Soc. B*, 148: 204–15.

104. — 1959. The First Mammals. *Discovery, Lond.*, 20(4): 144–151.

105. KIAER, J. 1924. The Downtonian Fauna of Norway. 1. Anaspida. *Skr. VidenskSelsk. Christiania*, 1. Mat-Naturv. K.1, 6: 1–139.

106. KOZLOWSKI, R. 1949. Les Graptolithes et quelques nouveaux groupes d'animaux du Tremadoc de la Pologne. *Palaeont. pol.*, 3: xii—1–235.

107. — 1961. Découverte d'un rhabdopleuride (Pterobranchia) ordovicien *Acta palaeont. pol.*, 6: 3–16.

108. — 1966. On the structure and relationships of graptolites. *J. Paleont.*, 40: 489–501.

109. — 1967. Sur certains fossiles Ordoviciens à test organique. *Acta palaeont. pol.*, 12: 99–132.

110. KUHN-SCHNYDER, E. 1952. Die Triasfauna der Tessiner Kalkalpen. XVII., *Askeptosaurus italicus* Nopesa. *Schweiz. palaeont. Abh.*, 69: 1–73.

111. KUHN-SCHNYDER, E. 1954. The origin of lizards. *Endeavour*, **13**: 213–9.

112. — 1962. La position des nothosauridés dans le système des reptiles. In *Problèmes actuels de Paléontologie (Évolution des Vertébrés). Colloques int. Cent. natn. Rech. scient.*, **104**: 135–44.

113. — 1963. Wege der Reptiliensystematik. *Paläont. Z.*, **37**: 61–87.

114. — 1964. Die Wirbeltierfauna der Trias der Tessiner Kalkalpen. *Geol. Rdsch.*, **53**: 393–412.

115. — 1965. Sind die Reptilien stammesgeschichtlich eine Einheit? *Umschau*, **1965**(5): 140–55.

116. LEAKEY, L. S. B. 1959. A new fossil skull from Olduvai. *Nature, Lond.*, **184**: 491–3.

117. LEAKEY, L. S. B., DAVIS, P. R., DAY, M. H. and NAPIER, J. R. 1964. Hominid fossils from Bed 1, Olduvai Gorge, Tanganyika. *Nature, Lond.*, **201**: 967–70;

TOBIAS, P. V. 1964. The Olduvai Bed 1 Hominine with special reference to its cranial capacity. *Nature*, **202**: 3–4;

LEAKEY, L. S. B. and LEAKEY, M. D. 1964. Recent discoveries of fossil hominids in Tanganyika: at Olduvai and near Lake Natron. *Nature*, **202**: 5–7;

LEAKEY, L. S. B., TOBIAS, P. B. and NAPIER, J. R. 1964. A new species of the genus *Homo* from Olduvai Gorge. *Nature*, **202**, 7–9;

OAKLEY, K. P. and CAMPBELL, B. G. 1964. Newly described Olduvai Hominid. *Nature*, **202**: 732;

TOBIAS, P. V. and VON KOENIGSWALD, G. H. R. 1964. A comparison between the Olduvai Hominines and those of Java and some implications for hominid phylogeny. *Nature*, **204**: 515–8;

ROBINSON, J. T. 1965. *Homo habilis* and the Australopithecines. *Nature*, **205**: 121–4;

TOBIAS, P. V. 1966. The distinctiveness of *Homo habilis*. *Nature*, **209**: 953–7;

— 1966. The distinctiveness of *Homo habilis*. *Nature*, **209**; 957–60.

118. LEAKEY, L. S. B. 1966. *Homo habilis*, Homo erectus and the Australopithecines. *Nature, Lond.*, **209**: 1279–81.

119. — 1967. An early Miocene member of Hominidae. *Nature, Lond.*, **213**: 155–63.

120. LESSERTISSEUR, J. and SIGOGNEAU, D. 1965. Sur l'acquisition des principales caractéristiques du squelette des mammifères. *Mammalia*, **29**: 95–168.

121. LINDSTRÖM, M. 1964. *Conodonts*. Elsevier, Amsterdam.

122. LINDSTRÖM, T. 1949. On the cranial nerves of the cyclostomes, with special reference to n. trigeminus. *Acta Zool.*, **30**: 315–458.

123. LORENZ, K. 1967. *On Aggression*. Methuen & Co. Ltd., London.

124. MILES, R. S. 1964. A reinterpretation of the visceral skeleton of Acanthodes. *Nature, Lond.*, **204**: 457–9.

125. — 1965. Some features in the cranial morphology of Acanthodians and the relationships of the Acanthodii. *Acta Zool.*, **46**: 233–55.

126. — 1967. Observations on the ptyctodont fish, *Rhamphodopsis* Watson. *J. Linn. Soc. (Zool.)*, **47**: 99–120.

127. MILLS, J. R. E. 1964. The dentitions of *Peramus* and *Amphitherium*. *Proc. Linn. Soc. Lond.*, **178**: 117–33.

128. MORRIS, D. 1967. *The Naked Ape*. Jonathan Cape, London.

129. NAPIER, J. 1962. The evolution of the hand. *Scient. Am.*, **207**(6): 56–62.

130. NAPIER, J. and CAMPBELL, B. 1964. The evolution of man. *Discovery*, **25**(6): 32–38.

131. NEWMAN, B. H. 1968a. Stance and gait of *Tyrannosaurus rex*. *J. Linn. Soc. (Zool)*, **48**.

132. — 1968b. The function of the forelimbs of *Tyrannosaurus rex*. *J. Linn. Soc. (Zool.)*, **48**.

133. NEWMAN, B. H. and TARLO, L. B. HALSTEAD. 1967. A giant marine reptile from Bedfordshire. *Animals*, **10**: 61–3.

134. NURSALL, J. R. 1962. On the origins of the major groups of animals. *Evolution*, **16**, 118–23.

135. — 1965. Man in Nature. *Queen's Quart.* **72**(1): 1–14.

136. OAKLEY, K. P. 1965. *Man the Tool-maker*. British Museum (Natural History), London.

137. OAKLEY, K. P. and CLARK, W. E. LE GROS, 1953. The solution of the Piltdown problem. *Bull. Brit. Mus. (Nat. Hist.) Geol.*, **2**: 139–46.

138. OBRUCHEV, D. 1941. Remains of Aspidosteus gen. nov. (Heterostraci) from the Upper Devonian of River Lovat. *Trans. Inst. Pal. Acad. Sci. URSS.* **8**(4):, 4–22.

139. —1943. A new restoration of Drepanaspis. *C. R. Acad. Sci. URSS*, **41**: 268–71.

140. — 1944. An attempted restoration of Psammolepis paradoxa. *C. R. Acad. Sci. URSS*, **42**: 143–5.

141. — 1945. The evolution of the Agnatha. *Zool. Zh.*, **24**: 257–72.

142. — 1964. Subclass Heterostraci (Pteraspides). *Osn. Paleont.*, **11**: 45–82.

143. OBRUCHEV, D. and MARK-KURIK, E. 1966. *Devonian Psammosteids (Agnatha, Psammosteidae) of the U.S.S.R.* Tallinn.

144. OLSON, E. C. 1961. The food chain and the origin of mammals. In Internat. Colloq. on the Evolution of Mammals. *Kon. Vlaamse Acad. Wetensch. Lett. Sch. Kunsten Belgie*, pt. 1, 97–116.

145. — 1962. Late Permian terrestrial vertebrates, U.S.A. and U.S.S.R. *Trans. Am. phil. Soc.*, **52**: 1–224.

146. — 1966. Community evolution and the origin of mammals. *Ecology*, **47**: 291–302.

147. ØRVIG, T. 1951. Histologic studies of Placoderms and fossil Elasmobranchs, 1: The endoskeleton, with remarks on the hard tissues of lower vertebrates in general. *Ark. Zool.*, Ser. 2, **2**: 321–454.

148. — 1957. Palaeohistological notes. 1. On the structure of the bone tissue in the scales of certain Palaeonisciformes. *Ark. Zool.*, Ser. 2, **10**: 481–90.

149 — 1958. Teeth and their hard tissues through the ages. *Zool. Rev.*, 1958(2/3): 29–63.

O

150. ØRVIG, T, 1960. New finds of Acanthodians, Arthrodines, Crossoptery-
gians, Ganoids and Dipnoans in the Upper Middle Devonian Calcareous
Flags (Oberer Plattenkalk) of the Bergisch Gladbach-Paffrath Trough.
(Part i). *Paläont. Z.*, **34**: 295–335.

151. — 1962. Y a-t-il une relation directe entre les arthrodires ptyctodontides
et les holocephales. In *Problèmes actuels de Paléontologie (Évolution des
Vertébrés)*. *Colloques int. Cent. natn. Rech. scient.*, **104**: 49–61.

152. — 1965. Palaeohistological notes. 2. Certain comments on the phyletic
significance of acellular bone tissue in early lower vertebrates. *Ark.
Zool.*, Ser. 2, **16**: 551–6.

153. — 1967. Phylogeny of tooth tissues; evolution of some calcified tissues in
early vertebrates. In *Structural and Chemical Organisation of Teeth*
(MILES, A. E. W., ed.). Academic Press, New York and London.

154. OSTROM, J. H. 1962. The cranial crests of hadrosaurian dinosaurs.
Postilla, **62**: 1–29.

155. PARRINGTON, F. R. 1961. The evolution of the mammalian femur. *Proc.
Zool. Soc. Lond.*, **137**: 285–98.

156. PATTERSON, C. 1965. The phylogeny of chimaeroids. *Phil. Trans. R. Soc.
B.* **249**, 101–219.

157. PAUTARD, F. G. E. 1961. Calcium, Phosphorus and the origin of back-
bones. *New Scientist*, **12**: 364–6.

158. — 1962. The molecular-biologic background to the evolution of bone.
Clin. Orthopaed., **24**: 230–44.

159. PERSSON, P. O. 1960. Lower Cretaceous Plesiosaurians (Rept.) from
Australia. *Lunds Univ. Arsskr. N.F. Adv. 2.* **56**(12): 1–23.

160. — 1963. A revision of the classification of the Plesiosauria with a synopsis
of the stratigraphical and geographical distribution of the group.
Lunds Univ. Arssk. (Acta Univ. Lund.) N.F. 2. **59**(1): 1–60.

161. PEYER, B. 1931. Die Triasfauna der Tessiner Kalkalpen. II. *Tanystropheus longobardicus* BASS. sp. *Abh. schweiz. paläont. Ges.*, **50**: 5–110.

162. PILBEAM, D. R. 1967. Man's earliest ancestors. *Science Jl.* **3**(2): 47–53.

163. PLOT, R. 1677. *The Natural History of Oxfordshire, being an essay toward
the natural history of England*. Oxford.

164. POLLARD, J. E. 1968. The gastric contents of an ichthyosaur from the
Lower Lias of Lyme Regis, Dorset. *Paleontology*, **11**: 376–88.

165. RAGLAND, LORD, 1949. *The origins of religion*. Watts & Co., London.

166. RHODES, F. H. T. 1954. The zoological affinities of the Conodonts. *Biol.
Rev.*, **29**: 419–52.

167. RITCHIE, A. 1960. A new interpretation of *Jamoytius kerwoodi* White.
Nature, Lond., **188**: 647–9.

168. — 1964. New Light on the morphology of the Norwegian Anaspida.
Skr. norske Vidensk-Akad., 1, Mat.-naturv. Kl., **14**: 1–35.

169. — 1968. New evidence on *Jamoytius kerwoodi* White, an important
ostracoderm from the Silurian of Lanarkshire, Scotland. *Palaeontology*,
11: 21–39.

170. ROBERTSON, J. D. 1957. The habitat of the early vertebrates. *Biol. Rev.*,
32: 156–87.

171. ROBINSON, P. L. 1957. The Mesozoic fissures of the Bristol Channel area and their vertebrate faunas. *J. Linn. Soc. (Zool.)*, **43**: 260–82.

172. — 1962. Gliding lizards from the Upper Keuper of Great Britain. *Proc. geol. Soc. Lond.*, **1601**: 137–46.

173. ROMER, A. S. 1933. Eurypterid influence on vertebrate history. *Science*, **78**: 114–7.

174. — 1942. Cartilage an embryonic adaptation. *Am. Nat.*, **76**: 394–404.

175. — 1957. Origin of the amniote egg. *Scient. Mon. N.Y.*, **85**: 57–63.

176. — 1958. Tetrapod limbs and early tetrapod life. *Evolution*, **12**: 365–9.

177. — 1958. Phylogeny and behaviour with special reference to vertebrate evolution. 48–75. In *Behaviour and Evolution*. (ROE, A. and SIMPSON, G. G., eds.). Yale University Press, New Haven.

178. — 1960. Explosive evolution. *Zool. Jb. Syst.* **88**: 79–90.

179. — 1963. The 'Ancient History' of bone. *Ann. N.Y. Acad. Sci.*, **109**: 168–176.

180. — 1964. The skeleton of the Lower Carboniferous labyrinthodont *Pholidogaster pisciformis*. *Bull. Mus. comp. Zool. Harv.*, **131**: 129–159.

181. — 1964. Bone in early vertebrates. In *Bone Biodynamics* (FROST, H. M., ed.). Little, Brown & Co. Detroit, pp. 13–40.

182. — 1967. Major steps in vertebrate evolution. *Science*, **158**: 1629–37.

183. SARGANT, W. 1957. *Battle for the Mind: a Physiology of Conversion and Brain-Washing*. Heinemann, London.

184. SHUTE, C. D. D. 1962. Evolution of vertebrae and cranio-spinal articulation. *J. Anat.*, **96**: 415.

185. SIMONS, E. L. 1961. The phyletic position of Ramapithecus. *Postilla*, **57**: 1–9.

186. — 1962. Fossil evidence relating to the early evolution of primate behaviour. *Ann. N.Y. Acad. Sci.*, **102**: 282–94.

187. — 1963. Some fallacies in the study of hominid phylogeny. *Science*, **141**: 879–89.

188. — 1964. The early relative of man. *Scient. Am.*, **211**(1): 51–62.

189. — 1965. New fossil apes from Egypt and the initial differentiation of Hominoidea. *Nature, Lond.*, **205**: 135–9.

190. SIMONS, E. L. and PILBEAM, D. R. 1965. Preliminary revision of the Dryopithecinae (Pongidae, Anthropoidea). *Folia primatol.*, **3**, 81–152.

191. SLIJPER, E. J. 1946. Comparative biologic-anatomical investigations on the vertebral column and spinal musculature of mammals. *Kon. Ned. Akad. Wet., Verh. (Tweede Sectie)*, **42**(5): 1–128.

192. — 1962. *Whales*. Hutchinson & Co. London.

193. SLOAN, R. E. and VAN VALEN, L. 1965. Cretaceous mammals from Montana. *Science*, **148**: 220–7.

194. SMITH, H. W. 1963. *From Fish to Philosopher*. Doubleday, New York.

195. SMITH, J. M. 1952. The importance of the nervous system in the evolution of animal flight. *Evolution*, **6**, 127–9.

196. SMITH, J. M. and SAVAGE, R. J. G. 1956. Some locomotory adaptations in mammals. *J. Linn. Soc. (Zool.)*, **42**: 603–22.

197. STENSIÖ, E. A. 1927. The Downtonian and Dittonian vertebrates of Spitsbergen. 1. Family Cephalaspidae. *Skr. Svalbard Ishavet.* **12**: 1–391.

198. — 1947. The sensory lines and dermal bones of the cheek in fishes and amphibians. *K. svenska VetensAkad. Handl.*, Ser. 3, **24**(3): 1–195.

199. — 1958. Les cyclostomes fossiles ou ostracodermes. In *Traité de Zoologie*, (GRASSÈ, P. P., ed.). **13**(1): 173–425.

200. — 1959. On the pectoral fin and shoulder girdle of the arthrodires. *K. Svenska VetensAkad. Handl.*, Ser. 4, **8**(1): 1–229.

201. — 1961. Permian Vertebrates. In RAASCH, G. O. (ed.): *Geology of the Artic*, 231–247, Univ. Toronto Press.

202. — 1962. Origine et nature des écailles placoïdes et des dents. In *Problèmes actuels de Paléontologie (Évolution des Vertèbrès). Colloques int. Cent. Natn. Rech. scient.*, **104**: 75–85.

203. — 1964a. The brain and cranial nerves in fossil, lower craniate vertebrates. *Skr. norske VidenskapsAkad.*, 1, Mat.-Naturv. Kl., **13**: 1–120.

204. — 1964b. Les cyclostomes fossiles ou Ostracodermes. In *Traité de Paléontologie* (PIVETEAU, J., ed.). **4**(1): 96–382.

205. STRAHAN, R. 1958. Speculations on the evolution of the agnathan head. *Proc. Cent. Bicent. Congr. Biol. Singapore*, 83–94.

206. SWINTON, W. E. 1939. A new Triassic Rhynchocephalian from Gloucestershire. *Ann. Mag. nat. Hist.*, Ser. 11, **4**: 591–4.

207. — 1965. *Fossil Birds*. British Museum (Natural History), London.

208. TARLO, B. J. 1965. The origin of sensitivity in dentine. *Roy. dent. Hosp. Mag.*, N.S. **1**(6): 11–3.

209. TARLO, B. J. and TARLO, L. B. HALSTEAD. 1964. The origin of tooth succession. *Roy. dent. Hosp. Mag.* N.S. **1**(4): 4–7.

210. — 1965. The origin of teeth. *Discovery, Lond.*, **26**(9): 20–26.

211. TARLO, L. B. HALSTEAD. 1958. The scapula of *Pliosaurus macromerus* Phillips. *Palaeontology*, **1**: 193–9.

212. — 1959. A new Middle Triassic reptile fauna from fissures in the Middle Devonian Limestones of Poland. *Proc. geol. Soc. Lond.* **1568**: 63–4.

213. — 1960a. The invertebrate origins of the vertebrates. *Rept. Int. Geol. Cong. XXI Sess.*, **22**: 113–23.

214. — 1960b. The Downtonian ostracoderm *Corvaspis kingi* Woodward, with notes on the development of dermal plates in the Heterostraci. *Palaeontology*, **3**: 217–26.

215. — 1961. *Rhinopteraspis cornubica* (McCoy), with notes on the classification and evolution of the pteraspids. *Acta palaeont. pol.* **4**: 367–400.

216. — 1962a. Ancient animals of the upland. *New Scientist*, **15**, 32–4.

217. — 1962b. Lignées évolutives chez les ostracodermes hetérostracés. In *Prcblèmes actuels de Paléontologie (Évolution des Vertébrés). Colloques int. Cent. Natn. Rech. scient.*, **104**: 31–7.

218. — 1962c. The classification and evolution of the Heterostraci. *Acta palaeont. pol.* **7**: 249–290.

219. — 1963. Aspidin: the precursor of bone. *Nature, Lond.* **199**: 46–8.

220. — 1964. The origin of bone. In *Bone and Tooth* (BLACKWOOD, H. J. J., ed.). Pergamon Press, Oxford.

221. — 1965. Psammosteiformes (Agnatha), a review with descriptions of new material from the Lower Devonian of Poland. I. General Part. *Palaeont. pol.* **13**: vii + 1-135.

222. — 1966. Psammosteiformes (Agnatha), a review with descriptions of new material from the Lower Devonian of Poland. II. Systematic Part. *Palaeont. pol.* **15**: ix + 1-168.

223. — 1967a. A fundamental symbol. *Penthouse*, **2**(7): 6; **2**(8): 6.

224. — 1967b. The tessellated pattern of dermal armour in the Heterostraci. *J. Linn. Soc. (Zool.)*, **47**: 45-54.

225. — 1967c. Triassic reptiles from the shores of Tethys. In *Aspects of Tethyan Biogeography* (ADAMS, C. G. and AGER, D. V., eds.). Systematics Association Publ. 7. London.

226. TARLO, L. B. HALSTEAD and TARLO, B. J. 1961. Histological sections of the dermal armour of psammosteid ostracoderms. *Proc. geol. Soc. Lond.*, **1593**: 3-4.

227. TARLO, L. B. HALSTEAD and WHITING, H. P. 1965. A new interpretation of the internal anatomy of the Heterostraci (Agnatha). *Nature, Lond.*, **206**: 148-50.

228. TAYLOR, E. K. 1963. *The Catholic Religion*. Catholic Enquiry Centre, London.

229. THALER, L. 1962. Empreintes de pas de dinosaures dans les Dolomies du Lias inférieur des Causses. *C.r.somm. Séanc. Soc. géol. Fr.*, **1962**(7): 190-2.

230. THOMSON, K. S. 1962. Rhipidistian classification in relation to the origin of the tetrapods. *Breviora*, **117**: 1-11.

231. — 1964a. The ancestry of the Tetrapods. *Sci. Prog., Lond.*, **521**: 451-459.

232. — 1964b. The comparative anatomy of the snout in rhipidistian fishes. *Bull. Mus. comp. Zool. Harv.*, **131**: 313-57.

233. — 1967. Notes on the relationships of the rhipidistian fishes and the ancestry of the tetrapods. *J. Paleont.*, **41**: 660-74.

234. TURING, A. M. 1952. The chemical basis of morphogenesis. *Phil. Trans. R. Soc. B*, **237**: 37-72.

235. WALKER, A. D. 1961. Triassic reptiles from the Elgin area: *Stagonolepis, Dasygnathus* and their allies. *Phil. Trans. R. Soc. B.* **244**: 103-204.

236. WARWICK, R. 1957. *Whillis's Elementary Anatomy and Physiology*. (4th edn.) Churchill Ltd., London.

237. WATSON, D. M. S. 1924. The elasmosaurid shoulder-girdle and fore-limb. *Proc. Zool. Soc. Lond.*, **2**: 885-917.

238. — 1926. The evolution and Origin of the Amphibia. *Phil. Trans. R. Soc.*, B. **214**: 189-257.

239. — 1937. The Acanthodian Fishes. *Phil. Trans. R. Soc.*, B, **228**: 49-146.

240. — 1954. A consideration of ostracoderms. *Phil. Trans. R. Soc.*, B, **238**: 1-25.

241. WATSON, D. M. S. 1957. On *Millerosaurus* and the early history of the sauropsid reptiles. *Phil. Trans. R. Soc.*, B, **240**: 325–400.

242. — 1961. Some additions to our knowledge of antiarchs. *Palaeontology*, **4**, 210–20.

243. WELLS, C. 1964. *Bones, bodies and disease*. Thames & Hudson, London.

244. WESTOLL, T. G. 1945. The paired fins of Placoderms. *Trans. R. Soc. Edinb.*, **61**: 381–98.

245. — 1967. *Radotina* and other tesserate fishes. *J. Linn. Soc. (Zool.).*, **47**: 83–98.

246. WHIMSTER, I. W. 1962. The mosaic nature of pigmentary change in diseased skin. *Annali ital. Derm. Sif.*, **16**: 357–84.

247. — 1965. An experimental approach to the problem of spottiness. *Br. J. Derm.*, **77**: 397–420.

248. WHITEAR, M. 1957. Some remarks on the Ascidian affinities of the vertebrates. *Ann. Mag. Nat. Hist.* (12), **10**: 338–48.

249. WHITING, H. P. and TARLO, L. B. HALSTEAD. 1965. The brain of the Heterostraci (Agnatha). *Nature, Lond.*, **207**: 829–31.

250. WICKLER, J. E. 1957. Neanderthal man. *Scient. Am.*, **197**(6).

251. YOUNG, C. C. 1964a. The Pseudosuchians in China. *Palaeont. sin.*, **151**: 1–205.

Index

Aardwark, 154
Acanthodian, 67–70, 72
Acellular bone, 41
Acetabulum, 123
Actinopterygian, 75, 78
Adam and Eve Complex, 101
Aepyornis, 145
Agnathan, 18, 24, 26, 57–9, 67, 68
Air bladder, 78
Allantois, 92
Althaspis, 19
Americans, 186
Ammocoete, 4, 57
Ammonite, 135
Amnion, 92
Amniote egg, 92, 94, 128, 130
Amphibian, 62, 77, 81–5, 87–9, 92–4, 96, 99, 103, 114, 139
Amphioxides larva, 7
Amphioxus, 2, 4
Amphistyly, 69
Anapsid, 97, 99, 100
Anaspid, 24, 58, 67
Ankylosaur, 124
Anteater, 151, 153
Antelope, 175
Anterior basal element (acanthodian), 69
Anthropoid, 171
Antiarch, 72, 78
Anuran, 80, 81, 93
Apatite, 43, 46, 47
Ape, 171–4, 182
Appendicularian, 7
Aphetohyoidean, 68, 69
Araeoscelida, 99, 101
Araeoscelidia, 101
Archaeopteryx, 143, 144
Archosaur, 99–101, 119, 120, 128, 139, 148, 149, 189
Arctocyonid, 162
Armadillo, 55, 153
Armour, 14, 27, 31, 33, 40, 67, 87

Art, 180, 183
Arthrodire, 70, 72
Arthropod, 136
Articular, 111, 112
Articular fossa, 156
Artiodactyl, 151, 158, 161
Ascidian, 7
Ascidian tadpole, 8
Askeptosaur, 136
Askeptosaurus, 115
Aspidin, 40–3
Aspidinoblast, 41, 42
Aspidinoclast, 43
Aspidinocyte, 42
Astralagus, 171
Australopithecine, 174, 175, 177, 178, 182
Australopithecus africanus, 173, 175
Australopithecus robustus, 175, 177
Axolotl, 87
Aye-aye, 39, 160

Baboon, 175, 186
Badger, 55, 151, 153, 164
Basals, 74, 75
Basidorsal, 89
Basiventral, 89
Bat, 151, 154
Beaked dolphin, 137, 156
Bear, 161, 162, 164
Bearing surface, 50, 51
Bénard cell, 31
Bipedal goat, 55, 56
Bird, 96, 102, 140, 143, 145, 147, 149–51, 154. 189
Boa-constrictor, 100
Bone, 14, 41–47
Bony fish, 61, 70, 75
Boundary layer lubrication, 50
Brachiopod, 130, 136
Brachiosaurus, 123, 124
Brain, 57, 60
Brain, fore, hind, mid, 37

Branchial arches, 68
Brontosaurus, 123, 148
Bunodont, 158, 161

Caenolestid, 151, 153
Calcaneum, 171
Calcification, 36
Calcified cartilage, 44, 45, 51
Calcium, 15
Calcium phosphate, 11, 15, 16
Californian lion, 164
Camel, 151
Canaliculae, 41
Cancellous bone, 40, 48
Canine, 105, 154, 158, 161, 163, 172, 173
Cannibalism, 178, 183
Cantilever, 52
Captorhinomorph, 103, 104, 114
Carnassial (teeth), 39, 162, 155
Carnivore, 39, 112, 114, 151, 154, 155, 160, 162–4
Cartilage, 40, 43–5, 51, 60, 150
Cartilaginous fish, 61, 69, 70
Catarrhine, 171
Cat, 39, 163, 164, 166
Cement, 158
Cementocytes, 42
Cementum, 42, 110
Central nervous system, 57
Centrum, 88, 89
Cephalaspid, 22, 24, 45, 57, 58, 61, 65, 66, 67
Cephalochordate, 2, 4
Cephalodiscid, 9
Cephalopod, 132, 134, 136, 137, 155, 156
Ceratopsian, 126
Cercopithecid, 171
Cerebellum, 57, 58, 60–62, 64, 107, 144, 150
Cerebral hemispheres, 107, 144, 150
Cerebrum, 57, 64
Cetacean, 39, 137
Chalicothere, 151
Cheetah, 55, 151, 153
Cheirolepis, 70
Chelonian, 97, 101, 148
Chevrotain, 159
Chimaera, 70
Chimpanzee, 172, 182, 184
Chin, 178
Choana, 79, 80

Choanichthyes, 79
Chondroblast, 45
Chordata, 2
Chorion, 92
Civet, 163
Cladoselache, 74
Clavicle, 168
Cleidoic egg, 92
Coelacanth, 78–80
Collagen, 41, 43, 46, 47, 51
Collagenous matrix, 27, 40, 41
Communists, 186
Compact bone, 40, 48, 49
Compression strut, 52
Condylarth, 147, 151, 155, 162
Conodontophoridia, 11, 12
Conodonts, 11
Corvaspis, 28
Cotylosaur, 97, 101
Crab-eating seal, 137, 156
Cranial nerves, 65
Craniata, 2, 6
Cranium, 68, 69, 97, 150, 163
Creodont, 39, 147, 162, 163
Crocodile, 39, 120, 132, 136, 147
Cro-Magnon man, 183
Crossopterygian, 62, 79, 168
Ctenurella, 70
Cusps, 38
Cuttlefish, 135
Cyathaspid, 19, 28
Cyclomorial, 36
Cyclostome, 6, 18, 19, 24, 26, 59

Deer, 55, 151
Deltatheridian, 147, 155, 162
Dental decay, 34, 164
Dental lamina, 110
Dentary, 111, 112, 159
Dentine, 27, 31, 33–5, 158, 160
Dentine tubercle, 27, 33, 34
Dentine tubules, 31, 34
Diapsid, 99, 100
Diarthrognathus, 112
Diastema, 158, 169
Diencephalon, 57–60
Dinosaur, 118, 119, 121, 127, 128, 143, 144, 146–50
Diplodocus, 123
Dipnoan, 79
Dodo, 145
Dog, 39, 162–6, 187
Dolphin, 137, 155

Doryaspis, 19
Draco, 139
Drepanaspis, 30
Dryopithecine, 171–3
Dryopithecus, 172

Echidna, 154
Eglonaspis, 21
Elasmobranchiomorph, 70
Elasmosaur, 132
Electric field, 24
Electric organ, 61
Elephant, 153, 159
Embolomere, 89, 90, 101, 189
Enamel, 31, 158, 160, 161
Endochondral ossification, 45
Enteropneust, 4
Entylonychid, 151
Eoreptilia, 88, 89
Eotheropsida, 101, 104
Epiphyseal plate, 150
Europrotaspis, 19
Euryapsid, 99, 100
Eurypterid, 14, 26
Eusauropsid, 115
Eusauropsida, 101
Extinction, 146, 189

Feathers, 143, 144
Femur, 107, 123
Fibreglass, 46, 47
Fibroblast, 42
Fins, 73, 74
Fire, 178
Fish, 68, 114, 128, 135, 155
Flamingo, 145
Fontanelle, 97
Food chain, 112, 114, 115, 137, 138, 147
Footprints, 123, 124
Forebrain, 61, 62, 64
Fox, 149, 162
Frog, 85–7, 93
Fur, 108

Galeopithecus, 153
Gavial, 39
Gibbon, 168, 169, 171
Gill arches, 65
Gill bars, 4
Gill lamellae, 66
Gill pouches, 66, 67
Gill rakers, 68

Gill slits, 4, 65, 67, 69
Glycogen gland, 124
Glyptodon, 153
Gondwanaland, 104, 105
Gorilla, 173, 182
Gnathostome, 2, 6
Graffiti, 180
Graptolite, 9
Great Auk, 145
Griffith cracks, 46, 47
Guerichosteus, 30

Hadrosaur, 126, 146
Haekel's Biogenic Law, 6
Hagfish, 13, 24, 26, 58–61
Hair, 108, 150
Hare, 160
Harding Sandstone, 12, 13
Haversian bone (system), 40, 49
Hedgehog, 146
Hemibranch, 67
Hemichordate, 2, 9
Herbivore, 112, 114, 158, 162, 163
Hesperornis, 144
Heterodontosaurus, 39, 159
Heterodontus, 38
Heterostracan, 18, 28, 31, 35, 40, 42, 43, 45, 59–61, 67
Hindbrain, 58, 61, 64
Hoatzin, 143
Holostean, 137
Hominoid, 171
Homodont, 39
Homo diluvii testis, 87
Homo erectus, 177, 178, 183
"*Homo habilis*", 175, 177
Homo neanderthalensis, 178
Homo sapiens, 177, 178
Horse, 55, 151, 158
Hound, 166
House dog, 166
Humerus, 84, 143
Hunters, 182
Hyaena, 163, 175
Hyaenodont, 155, 162, 163
Hyobranchial skeleton, 86
Hyoidean arch, 65, 68, 69
Hyoidean gill, 69
Hyoidean gill slit, 68, 69
Hyoidean gill cover, 70
Hyoidean pouch, 66
Hyoidean segment, 65
Hyomandibular, 69, 70, 84

Hypophysis, 57
Hypsodont, 158, 159

Icarosaurus, 117, 139
Ichthyopterygia, 101
Ichthyornis, 145
Ichthyosaur, 38, 96, 99, 128, 130, 132, 135, 136
Ichthyostega, 83
Ichthyostegid, 83–85, 88, 97
Ictidosaur, 39
Ilium, 90, 107
Incisor, 153, 158, 159, 161, 171, 173
Insectivore, 151, 162, 167, 169
Intercentrum, 88, 89
Interdorsal, 89
Interventral, 89
Ischium, 107

Jamoytius, 25, 26, 45
Jaw, 46, 65, 67–9, 85, 94–6, 100, 111, 112, 115, 150
Jews, 186
Joint, cartilaginous, 49
Joint, fibrous, 49
Joint, osteoarthritic, 51
Joint, synovial, 50
Jugal, 97, 100

Kidney, 12, 13
Killer whale, 137, 138, 156
Kotlassia, 91
Kuehneosaurus, 117
Kuehneosuchus, 117

Labyrinthodont, 189
Lacunae, 41
Lagomorph, 39, 151, 160
Lamellibranch, 136
Laminar bone, 49
Laminar flow, 137
Lamprey, 23–6, 45, 58, 60, 61, 66, 67
Larvacean, 7
Larval evolution, 6, 7
Larval lamprey, 4, 57
Larval tunicate, 2, 4
Lateral fin-fold, 72
Latimeria, 79
Lemur, 171
Lepidomoria, 36
Lepidomorial Theory, 36–8
Lepidosaur, 100, 101, 119, 128
Lepidotrichia, 75

Lepospondyl, 81, 87
Lever, first order, 53
Lever, second order, 53
Lever, third order, 53
Lissamphibia, 81
Lizard, 99, 100, 114, 115, 117, 118, 120, 139, 147
Llama, 151
Lobe-fin, 74, 78
Lophodont, 158
Lubrication, boundary layer, 50
Lubrication, hydrodynamic, 51
Lungfish, 78, 79
Lungs, 78, 79, 87

Macrauchenid litoptern, 151
Mammal, 94, 96, 101, 102, 110, 112, 118, 119, 127, 137, 146, 150, 167, 182, 189
Mammal-like reptile, 94, 96, 99, 101, 103, 105, 110, 112, 114, 115, 117, 119
Mammary glands, 108
Man, 39, 138, 148, 153, 164–7, 169, 171–4, 177, 178, 182, 184, 185, 187–9
Mandibular arch, 65, 67, 69
Mandibular condyle, 160
Mandibular segment, 65
Marsupial, 147, 151, 153
Marsupial flying squirrel, 153
Marsupial mole, 153
Masseter, 112, 156, 160, 161
Mastodon, 160
Maxilla, 105–7, 109
Mechanical advantage, 53, 55, 133
Medulla oblongata, 58, 60
Meninge, 60
Mesencephalon, 57, 58
Mesonychid, 155, 162
Mesopterygia, 74
Mesosaur, 39, 99, 101, 120
Metameric segmentation, 65
Metapterygia, 74, 75
Metapterygial stem, 75
Metencephalon, 57
Methodists, 186
Miacid, 162–4
Mice, 164
Mid brain, 60–2, 64
Millerosaur, 99, 119
Millers, 182
Moa, 145

Molar, 154, 158, 163
Monkey, 171
Morganucodon, 112
Mosaic pattern, 30
Mosasaur, 38, 135–7, 145
Multituberculate, 160
Myelencephalon, 38
Myosepta, 89
Myotome, 89
Mystacete, 137
Myxinoid, 13

Nails, 168, 171
Nasal, 126
Nasohypophyseal opening, 58
Nazis, 186
Neanderthal man, 173, 180
Neck, 107
Necrolemur, 171
Neoteny, 7, 44
Newt, 87
Nothosaur, 101, 130, 132, 136
Notochord, 2, 7
Nutcracker man, 174

Obruchevia, 22
Occipital condyle, 89
Odontoblast, 27, 34
Odontocete, 137
Olfactory lobes, 57, 58, 61, 62
Oligopithecus, 171
Opercular bones, 84
Opossum, 153
Optic lobes, 144
Orang, 168
Oreopithecus, 169
Ornithischian, 121, 124, 126, 143
Ornithopod, 124, 126, 143
Osteoarthritis, 51, 179
Osteoblast, 42, 43, 45
Osteoclast, 43, 49
Osteocyte, 42, 43
Osteodontokeratic culture, 175
Osteoloepidiformes, 80
Osteolepid, 83
Osteostracan, 22
Ostracoderm, 6, 16, 18, 24, 26
Otic notch, 84, 96
Otter, 120, 164
Oxyaenid, 155, 162

Palatine, 107
Panda, 161

Pangolin, 154
Paramammal, 103, 105–8, 110, 111, 114, 115, 117, 120, 128, 142, 168, 189
Paramammalia, 101
Parapsid, 99
Parasphenoid, 69
Parietal, 83, 99, 100
Parkinson's Law, 151
Passenger pigeon, 145
Patagium, 139
Peccary, 153
Pectoral girdle, 133
Pelvic girdle, 107
Pelycosaur, 103–5
Pentadactyl limb, 84
Perissodactyl, 158
Petromyzonid, 23
Phalangeal formula, 89
Pharynx, 78
Pharynx, perforated, 2, 4
Phosphatases, 45
Phosphate, 15
Phosphate cycle, 16
Phosphates, 16
Phytosaur, 121
Pig, 161, 162
Pike, 39
Piltdown man, 173, 174, 179
Pineal organ, 57, 60
Pinniped, 137
Pisces, 100
Pithecanthropoid, 177
Placodont, 38, 96, 99, 101, 130, 163
Platyrrhine, 171
Pleromic dentine, 34
Plesiadapis, 169
Plesiodraco, 117
Plesiosaur, 39, 96, 99, 101, 132, 134–6
Pleurocentrum, 88
Pliopithecus, 171
Pliosaur, 132, 134–6
Pneumatic bone, 140
Pogonophore, 2, 9
Pongid, 171
Porcupine, 153
Porolepidiformes, 80
Porolepid, 81
Port Jackson shark, 38
Post-frontal, 99
Post-orbital, 97, 100
Post-orbital bar, 150, 168, 169

Potters, 182
Premandibular arch, 67
Premandibular segment, 65
Premandibular somite, 60
Premolar, 154, 158, 173
Pre-orbital fenestra, 119
Pre-otic somite, 60
Pre-spiracular gill pouch, 65
Primate, 147, 153, 162, 167–9, 189
Proboscidean, 159
Proboscis, 159
Proganosauria, 101
Propliopithecus, 171
Propodial, 132, 133, 135
Propterygia, 74
Prosimian, 169, 171
Proterothere litoptern, 151, 153
Protoascidian, 9
Protobatrachus, 85
Protoceratops, 148
Protorosauria, 101
Psammosteid, 21, 30, 33, 34
Psammosteus, 22
Pteranodon, 142, 143
Pteraspid, 19, 30
Pterobranch, 4, 9
Pterygoid, 156, 161
Pterosaur, 139, 140, 142–4, 151, 189
Ptyctodont, 70
Pudendal graffiti, 180
Pustules, 30
Pycnosteus, 21
Pyrothere, 153

Quadrate, 95, 96, 100, 111, 112
Quadratojugal, 97, 100

Rabbit, 160
Raccoon, 161, 164
Radials, 74, 75
Radius, 143, 165, 168
Ramapithecus, 171–4, 182
Rat, 164,
Ray, 70, 130
Reinforced concrete, 46
Religion, 178
Reptilia, 100–2
Reptile, 89, 92–94, 96, 103, 110, 112, 136, 137, 139, 149, 182
Resegmentation, 89
Rhabdopleurid, 9
Rhachitome, 88, 89
Rhinopteraspis, 19

Rhipidistian, 63, 78–80, 82, 84, 88
Rhynchocephalian, 100, 115, 117, 150
Rhynchosaur, 115
Roc, 145
Rodent, 39, 151, 160, 161, 169
Ruminant, 158

Sabre-tooth, 163, 164
Sacral ganglion, 124
Sacrum, 85, 90
Salamander, 87
Salivary glands, 69
Saurischian, 121, 123
Sauropod, 123
Sauropsid, 96, 97, 99, 100, 114
Sauropterygian, 99–101
Scale, placoid, 35, 36
Sclerotome, 89
Scrotum humanum, 121
Seal, 137, 155
Sea squirt, 2
Secondary dentine, 34
Secondary palate, 107, 109, 121
Seymouria, 91
Seymouriamorph, 89–91
Shark, 62, 74, 75, 110, 136
Sharpey's fibres, 41
Sheepdog, 166
Shrew, 146
Skate, 70, 130
Skull, 62
Sloth, 153
Snake, 100, 118, 147
Snout, 62
Solitary, 145
Somites, 67
Soul, 183
Sperm whale, 137, 156
Spiny anteater, 154
Spiracle, 69
Spiracular cleft, 84
Squamosal, 97, 100, 111, 112, 150, 156, 159
Stagonolepid, 121
Stapes, 69
Stegosaurus, 124
Stereospondyl, 88, 89
Stoat, 164
Stomochord, 2
Struthiomimus, 148, 149
Supratemporal, 99
Swift, 143
Synapsid, 97, 99–101

Synaptosaur, 99
Synchronomorial, 36

Tadpole, 85, 91, 94
Tadpole larva, 9
Tail, post-anal, 2
Tanystropheus, 115
Tapir, 158
Tarsier, 171
Tasmanian Devil, 153
Taurodont molar, 180
Tectum, 62
Teeth, 33, 35, 38
Telencephalon, 57–9, 61
Teleost, 136, 137, 147
Temporal opening, 97, 99, 100, 103, 115, 150
Temporalis, 112, 156, 160, 161
Terrapin, 97
Terrazzo, 27, 28
Tessellated pattern, 31
Tesserae, 27, 28, 30
Tethys, 104, 105
Tetrapod, 79, 80, 82
Thaliacean, 7
Thelodont, 19
Therapsid, 103, 104
Theropod, 121, 124
Theropsid, 96, 97, 100, 103, 110, 114, 127
Thomashuxleya, 151
Thumb, 168, 169, 175
Thylacine wolf, 153
Tibia, 123
Toad, 85
Tolypelepis, 28
Tongue, 80
Tooth cusps, 36
Tortoise, 148
Toxodont, 151
Trabeculae, 40–42, 47, 48
Traquairaspid, 30
Travelling salesmen, 182
Tree-shrew, 154, 169
Tribosphenic molar, 154, 158

Triceratops, 148
Trilophodont, 159
Trilophosauria, 101
Trituberculosectorial molar, 154
Tritylodont, 160
Tuatara, 100
Tubules, dentine, 31, 34
Tunicate, 2, 4, 7
Tupaia, 169
Turbinal bones, 108
Turtle, 148
Tympanic cavity, 112
Tympanic membrane, 96
Typothere, 39, 151, 160
Tyrannosaurus, 121

Ulna, 165, 168
Ungulate, 151, 154, 160, 165
Urodele, 80, 87
Urostyle, 85

Vampire bat, 155
Venuses, 180
Vertebrae, 83, 88
Vertebral column, 85, 121, 123
Vibrissae, 109
Visceral arches, 45, 66, 67
Viverrid, 163

Walrus, 38, 137, 156
Warthog, 161
Weapon, 174, 175, 182, 184
Weasel, 162, 164,
Weavers, 182
Whales, 137, 138, 155
Wolverine, 164
Woman, 164, 182, 187, 188
Wormian bones, 30

Yolk sac, 92

Zalambodont molar, 154
Zooplankton, 136–8
Zygomatic arch, 150
Zygopophyses, 90

DATE DUE